Student nurse in psychiatric unit corridor, St Clement's Hospital, Bow, c1970
(Royal London Hospital Archives: SC/P/15)

TSO

information & publishing solutions

Published by TSO (The Stationery Office) and available from:

Online
www.tsoshop.co.uk

Mail, Telephone, Fax & Email
TSO
PO Box 29, Norwich, NR3 1GN
Telephone orders/General enquiries: 0870 600 5522
Fax orders: 0870 600 5533
Email: book.orders@tso.co.uk
Textphone 0870 240 3701

TSO Shops
16 Arthur Street, Belfast BT1 4GD
028 9023 8451 Fax 028 9023 5401
71 Lothian Road, Edinburgh EH3 9AZ
0870 606 5566 Fax 0870 606 5588

TSO@Blackwell and other Accredited Agents

Applications for reproduction should be made in writing to Sugar Media Ltd,
Studio 65-66, The Maltings, 169 Tower Bridge Road, London SE1 3LJ

A CIP catalogue record for this book is available from the British Library

A Library of Congress CIP catalogue record has been applied for

First published 2006
Second impression 2007
ISBN 978-0-11-322721-1

Printed in the United Kingdom for The Stationery Office

Author: Ann Kramer
Interviews: Abigail Bernard
Design: Jon-Paul Daly jp@sugarmedia.co.uk
For Sugar Media Ltd ©: Isabel Appio & Ian Thomas
Studio 65-66, The Maltings, 169 Tower Bridge Road, London SE1 3LJ

This book is
jointly funded
by the Department
of Health

Cover Picture: Part of a contingent of 1,000 West Indian immigrants with their luggage at Paddington Station in London, 9 April 1956; this was the largest single group to arrive in Britain since immigration from the Caribbean began in the early 1950s (© Photo by Edward Miller/Keystone/Getty Images)

Mile End Hospital: presentation of training certificates and prizes to nurses, 1970
(Royal London Hospital Archives: ME/P/14)

Many rivers to cross
Caribbean People in the NHS 1948-69

Author: Ann Kramer
Interviews: Abigail Bernard

Published by Sugar Media Limited ©

A British Council worker helps a West Indian immigrant along the platform at Victoria Station, 9 June 1956

Preface
Patricia Hewitt MP

I am proud to be associated with this book. *Many rivers to cross* shows how people from the Caribbean made an enormous and vital contribution to the NHS in its early days and subsequently. The individual stories told in this book bear testament not only to the determination and professionalism of the *Windrush* generation, but also to their resolve to succeed in another country and to tackle and overcome whatever discrimination came their way.

Reading this book makes me more determined than ever to ensure that the NHS continues to strive to be a world-class service. A service that can be readily accessed by individuals from all communities, who can expect fast and fair services appropriate to their individual needs. A service that treats its workforce with dignity and respect, where people from whatever background can develop and progress in their chosen career. A service to be proud of.

Rt Hon Patricia Hewitt MP
Secretary of State for Health

May 2006

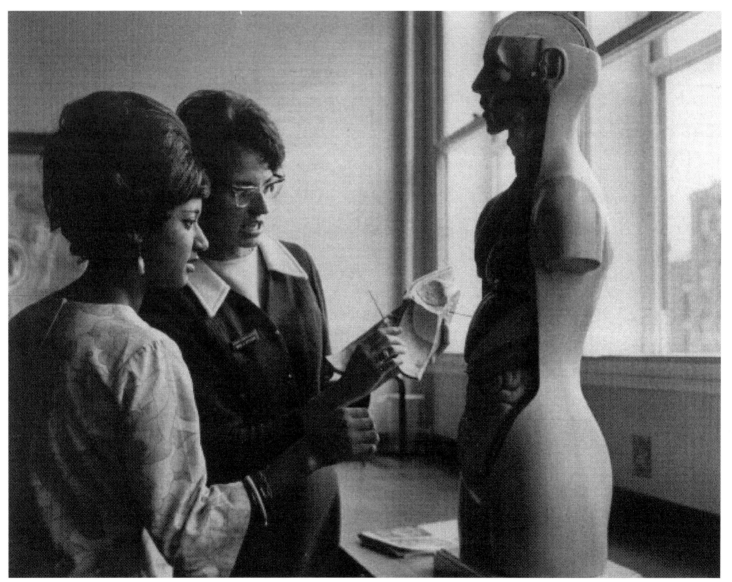

Miss V Styles, a nursing careers adviser, explains some aspects of anatomy to Miss Authrine Patterson, Jamaica Farm Queen, in the Princess Alexandra School of Nursing, London Hospital, September 1970 (Royal London Hospital Archives LH/P/2/42)

Foreword
Sir Ian Carruthers

Sir Ian Carruthers OBE
Acting NHS Chief Executive
Department of Health

I am privileged and delighted to be associated with this book for two reasons. First, it provides a welcome opportunity to say thank you and to celebrate the significant contribution people of Caribbean origin have made – and continue to make – to the NHS. Second, I know the inspirational stories contained within these pages can only strengthen our hand as we strive to attract new generations of people from a diversity of backgrounds to work in the NHS, helping us provide a better service to patients.

What makes the NHS so special as an employer is the rich tapestry of cultures represented by its 1.3 million staff. By making that long journey into the unknown on boats like the *SS Empire Windrush* all those years ago, Caribbean people were not only critical to the success of the NHS in its formative years but also created a lasting legacy of diversity in its employees. Today the NHS is the single largest employer of people from black and minority ethnic backgrounds with over 14 per cent of staff, that's 183,300 people.

This is encouraging. As a public service it is important that the make-up of our staff broadly reflects the society we service. But that is not an end in itself: it's about improving the service we provide. In this respect, we know there is more to do. For instance, people from a South Asian background are six times more likely than the majority of the population to have type 1 diabetes and that satisfaction rates as patients or as staff are lower from people of black and minority communities than they are from the majority population.

Having the right mix of staff is helping the NHS to improve, but it is not just about numbers. The perception of the NHS by many as being 'snow-capped' – it gets whiter the higher up in the organisation you get – is largely right. Our challenge is to ensure that staff from black and minority communities feel empowered and supported and see that they can develop to become leaders in the future. This will in turn help better equip us to attract black and minority staff and better serve those communities.

For this reason, my predecessor Sir Nigel Crisp challenged NHS leaders to give greater prominence to race equality as part of the drive to improve health. It addresses five service delivery and five workforce issues. For example, NHS leaders are now carrying out equity audits to look at which part of their populations the NHS should be reaching better.

Senior leaders in the NHS and Department of Health were challenged to mentor someone from the black and minority ethnic community. The target was for 500 mentoring

Sir Nigel Crisp, former NHS Chief Executive

arrangements. In fact, around 900 materialised.

It was also because of Sir Nigel's personal backing that the Caribbean book project got off the ground. It was because of his unstinting support that the book is now published as *Many rivers to cross*. Through the Caribbean book project, the leadership and race equality action plan and a number of other initiatives, Sir Nigel demonstrated an unequivocal and strong commitment to people from black and minority ethnic backgrounds to ensure that they, be they patients or staff, got as good a deal as anyone else. He set an example of commitment and leadership we should all follow.

This book is about celebrating the past and looking forward to a promising future. I am proud of the staff who work in the NHS and the service it provides. But most of all, I am proud of our constant efforts to improve it. Like those early migrants we are on a journey and – with that same spirit of endeavour and inclusivity that are the bedrock of the NHS – we will surely get there. Overall, we are trying to make sure that in the future, the NHS is an absolutely inclusive organisation and that everyone can rise through the NHS on the basis of talent and hard work.

May 2006

Part of a group of 1,000 West Indian immigrants with their luggage at Paddington Station in London, 9 April 1956; this was the largest single group to arrive in Britain since immigration from the Caribbean began in the late 1940s

Contents

Introduction

In 1945 World War Two finally ended. In Britain, a Labour government came to power with a programme of radical social reforms that would create a welfare state for postwar Britain. Central to these reforms was the National Health Service (NHS) – the world's first comprehensive health service, which provided health care free for every British citizen, according to need rather than means.

A Jamaican air gunner serving in an Army Cooperation Command of the Royal Air Force

© Imperial War Museum

From the very beginning, nurses, doctors and other hospital workers from the Caribbean played a major role in the NHS. Then, as now, the NHS would not have been able to function without them. Yet their role and contributions are not covered in social or political histories of the NHS – they have been left out. This book aims to redress the imbalance and place Caribbean nurses, doctors and ancillary workers where they belong, in the forefront of the development of the NHS.

This book looks at the origins of the NHS, how West Indian nurses and health workers were recruited to work in NHS hospitals, the work they did and their experiences. It includes reminiscences from more than 30 Caribbean women and men – nurses, doctors, midwives, health visitors, cooks and carpenters – who travelled from the Caribbean to staff British hospitals from the late 1940s through to the 1960s. They were interviewed specifically for this book. Their voices and experiences give a vivid picture of what life was like for them in the UK and the NHS at that time, and how their determination and dedication enabled the NHS to provide its essential service.

Origins of the NHS

On 5 July 1948 the NHS came into being. For the first time ever, people in Britain could access healthcare completely free at the point of delivery, no matter what their status and without need for

"SINCE THE HEALTH SERVICE CAME INTO BEING IN 1948, ITS VERY BACKBONE HAS DEPENDED ON A STEADY STREAM OF IMPORTED, TRAINED HEALTH PROFESSIONALS. THE NHS WOULD NEVER HAVE BEEN ABLE TO MEET BRITAIN'S GROWING HEALTH NEEDS WITHOUT THEM." Trevor Phillips, Chair of the Commission for Racial Equality

The first NHS patient, Sylvia Diggory, née Beckingham, with Aneurin Bevan at Park Hospital (now Trafford General), 5 July 1948

any means test. It was one of the major social achievements of 20th-century Britain and it changed people's lives.

There had been plans to create a national health service in Britain for some years. In 1942, at the height of World War Two, the British economist William Beveridge produced a report – known as the Beveridge Report – that laid the basis for what became Britain's welfare state. Beveridge proposed that there should be an all-out attack on the 'five giants' of Want, Disease, Ignorance, Squalor and Idleness. As part of the postwar reconstruction, a welfare system would be introduced, paid for out of taxation and national insurance, that would provide for citizens from 'cradle to grave'. A national health service was fundamental to this vision of a caring society.

Paying for medical care

Before 1948 people in Britain either paid for their health care or went without. People had to pay for doctors, hospitals and medicines. Working men on low incomes could access free health care through insurance schemes that had been introduced in 1911, but these did not cover their wives or families. The very poor could have hospital care for free but they had to undergo a humiliating means test. People avoided calling the doctor, choosing to treat themselves, visit pharmacies or go without treatment.

There were two main kinds of hospitals: voluntary hospitals, including the teaching hospitals, and local authority or municipal hospitals. Voluntary hospitals provided care for acute conditions and were funded through fees, charitable donations and fund-raising events. Local authority hospitals treated the elderly, those with chronic conditions such as infectious diseases and those with mental illness. They were funded

Jamaicans reading a newspaper while on board the ex-troopship SS Empire Windrush *bound for Tilbury docks in Essex, 22 June 1948*

Many rivers to cross

through the rates and government grants. Many hospitals were old and in serious need of repair. Some were converted workhouses.

There had been concerns about the health of the nation for some years. Health had been improving since the mid-19th century but there were still pressing health needs. In 1939 about one child out of every twenty died before their first birthday. Infectious diseases such as pneumonia, meningitis, diphtheria, tuberculosis and polio were major killers.

Increasingly, it was felt that the introduction of a national health service, funded from taxation and national insurance, would mean that everyone would receive health care equally, that the ramshackle hospital service would be organised more efficiently and that the nation's health would improve dramatically. But this could only happen if, as in education, the state took responsibility for health care. Aneurin Bevan, Minister for Health, drew up plans for a health service, which were outlined in the National Health Act of 1946. The aim was to establish a 'comprehensive health service to secure the improvement in the physical and mental health of the people … and the prevention, diagnosis and treatment of illness.' Services were to be 'free of charge'.

Taking over the hospitals

On 5 July 1948 the National Health Service came into being. The government became caretaker of 2,688 hospitals – 1,143 voluntary hospitals providing some 90,000 beds and 1,545 municipal hospitals with about 390,000 beds, of which 190,000 were in hospitals for the mentally ill. The NHS was launched as a single organisation based on 14 regional hospital boards. There were three parts: hospital services; family doctors, dentists, opticians and pharmacists; and local authority health services, including community nursing and health visiting. Immediately, millions signed on with a doctor. Inpatient care soared from 2.9 million people in 1949 to 3.5 million in 1953, while outpatient care rose from 6.1 million people in 1949 to 6.7 million in 1953.

Difficulties and labour shortages

The new NHS was far more costly than anyone could have expected but there was a wish for it to succeed. The government's first priority was to reorganise the hospitals. However, Britain was suffering the after-effects of war: food was rationed, the economy needed rebuilding and bomb damage meant resources were needed to build new homes rather than new hospitals. There was also a serious labour shortage. To rebuild the country, Britain needed more workers, particularly in low-paid jobs that white British people were not willing to do. The new health service was no exception. It was desperately short of staff – nurses, midwives, ancillary workers, cleaners, cooks and porters.

An urgent national need

In 1945 a government report produced by Aneurin Bevan and others – Staffing the Hospitals: An Urgent National Need – highlighted a 'woeful' shortage of nursing staff. According to the report there was an immediate need for at least 30,000 more nurses and midwives and about 12,000 domestic and other hospital workers. Without them the new NHS would not be able to function. Two years later the trade union COHSE called on the government to initiate a national recruiting campaign 'to meet the grave shortage of nursing personnel'. In 1948 the report of the working party on the Employment in the United Kingdom of Surplus Colonial Labour stated that there were 54,000 vacancies for nursing staff in Britain. The most serious shortages were in hospitals for the chronic sick, in mental hospitals and in geriatric nursing, none of which were particularly popular areas of nursing.

Recruitment drives

From 1948 the British government funded recruitment drives to attract qualified nurses, trainees, domestic workers and others into the hospitals. Recruitment took place in Britain and overseas. The response from British-born women was poor. More than 700 vacancies were advertised in Tottenham, for instance, but there were only 17 enquiries. During the war women had flocked to nursing as part of the war effort. Afterwards most married women returned to the home. Young, single, British-born women were more interested in taking up better-paid opportunities that were opening up to women, such as secretarial work, teaching or work in the civil service. Nursing, with its long hours, low pay and strict discipline, was far less appealing.

Recruiting from the Caribbean

In 1949 the Ministries of Health and Labour, together with the Colonial Office, the General Nursing Council (GNC) and the Royal College of Nursing (RCN), began a deliberate policy of recruiting from the British colonies, particularly the West Indies. Recruitment was aimed at three main categories of workers: hospital auxiliary staff (orderlies, receptionists, cooks, pantry workers, and telephonists), nurses or trainee nurses, and domestic workers, such as laundry workers.

From the late 1940s and throughout the 1950s, advertisements appeared in the nursing press encouraging applicants from the colonies. In the Caribbean, newspapers such as the *Barbados Advocate* or *Barbados Beacon* ran advertisements inviting young women students to apply to train as nurses in Britain. There were also advertisements for ward orderlies, cooks, maids and other domestic staff. In 1949, for instance, the *Barbados Beacon* advertised for 31 women to work as nursing auxiliaries in hospitals in Bristol, Cardiff, Dartford, Edinburgh, Lincolnshire, Loughborough,

Health Pioneers

The history of the Caribbean contribution to UK's health sector is long and distinguished. Trailblazers who predated the NHS include:

Mary Seacole

MARY SEACOLE (1805–81) Born in Kingston, Jamaica, Mary Seacole had a Scottish father and Caribbean mother. Well educated, she learned nursing from her mother, who taught her traditional therapies brought over from Africa by slaves. In 1854, when the Crimean War broke out, Mary Seacole offered her services as a nurse to the British Army but was rejected, probably because of her colour. Using her own money, she went to the Crimea, where she nursed the wounded on the battlefield, often under fire. Following the war, Mary Seacole was penniless and in debt. Influential friends raised money for her. Her autobiography, *Wonderful Adventures of Mrs Mary Seacole in Many Lands*, published in 1857, became a bestseller. Today, there is an award named after her for black and ethnic minority nurses.

Dr John Alcindor

DR JOHN ALCINDOR (1873–1924) Trinidadian-born John Alcindor attended medical school in Edinburgh, graduating with first-class honours in 1899. He worked in many hospitals and in 1907 established his own practice in Paddington, one of the first black general practices in the UK. He was an active member and president of the African Progress Union. He wrote and published articles on various health issues, particularly cancer and TB.

DR HAROLD MOODY (1882–1947) Born in Jamaica, Dr Harold Moody moved to London in 1904. He studied medicine at King's College but racial prejudice prevented him from obtaining a hospital post. Eventually he set up his own practice in Peckham. He worked tirelessly for others, helping black people to find accommodation and work. In 1931 he set up the influential League of Coloured Peoples.

Dr Harold Moody

DAVID THOMAS PITT (1913–94) An accomplished and distinguished doctor and politician, David Pitt was born in Grenada. In 1932 he won Grenada's only overseas scholarship to attend the University of Edinburgh medical school. He graduated with honours and returned to the West Indies, where he practised medicine. In 1943 he helped found the West Indian National Party, lobbying the British parliament for independence. In 1950 he settled in the UK and established a medical practice in London. His patients included many well-known Caribbean figures, such as Diane Abbott, Trevor Phillips and Darcus Howe. Throughout the 1960s and 1970s he campaigned to improve race relations. He stood for parliament in 1959, the first West Indian black to do so. Racism

David Thomas Pitt

marred the election and Pitt did not win the seat. In 1974 he became chair of the Greater London Council (GLC) and in 1975 was appointed to the House of Lords. From 1985–86, he was president of the British Medical Association (BMA).

Elizabeth Anionwu

More recent health pioneers include **ELIZABETH ANIONWU**, Professor of Nursing, Head of the Mary Seacole Centre for Nursing Practice at Thames Valley University, who has campaigned for BME nurses, and the late **DAPHNE STEEL**, Britain's first black matron.

Daphne Steele

Manchester and North Staffordshire. Candidates had to be aged 18 to 30, literate and prepared to sign a three-year contract.

Working together

For Britain, the colonies were an important source of much-needed nurses and ancillary workers. Senior British matrons went to the Caribbean to recruit nurses. So too did Enoch Powell, who later became notorious for his attacks on black immigrants. In 1951 Florence Udell, Colonial Office Chief Nursing Officer (COCNO), went to the Caribbean to meet with senior nursing officers. Colonial governors, the Ministries of Health and Labour and the Colonial Office worked together to recruit and select women workers for employment in British hospitals. The aim of recruitment policy in Britain and the Caribbean was to fill vacancies in British hospitals but also to train nurses who would return to the Caribbean to help develop health services there.

Selection procedures

By 1955, 16 British colonies had set up selection and recruitment procedures to ensure a steady flow of colonial nursing candidates for the NHS. Within the Caribbean, there were official recruitment schemes in Barbados, British Guiana (now Guyana), Jamaica, the Leeward Islands (Antigua, Montserrat and St Kitts), Trinidad & Tobago and the Windward Islands (Dominica,

Charlie Gomm, LT Recruitment Officer, seen interviewing the first batch of Caribbean applicants for work with London Transport, Barbados, 1956

Grenada, St Lucia and St Vincent). Individual British hospitals as well as regional hospital boards often advertised directly for staff. In 1956, for instance, the South-West Metropolitan Regional Hospital Board put out a request for 'West Indians as nursing auxiliaries, nursing assistants and possibly student nurses' who could be placed in specially selected hospitals.

Caribbean women wishing to apply for nurse training in Britain had to be aged 19–30, qualified to matriculation level (equivalent to today's GCSEs) and English-speaking. Typically, a candidate either responded to an advertisement or applied directly to matrons in NHS hospitals in Britain. Candidates put in a written application, which went to a selection board together with testimonials or references. Successful applicants were interviewed and some had to do a short

Left: A British Council worker talking to a West Indian immigrant at Victoria Station, London, 9 June 1953
Below: Three Jamaican immigrants arrive at Tilbury on 22 June 1948 on board the ex-troopship SS Empire Windrush. The arrival of the Windrush was a major landmark in the development of multicultural Britain.

© Photo by Haywood Magee/Picture Post/Getty Images

© Photo by Douglas Miller/Getty Images

A poster advertising furnished accommodation in South London

© pic Courtesy of Lambeth Archives

General Nursing Council-approved preliminary training course. Application forms were sent to the Colonial Office in Britain for approval. There was some government sponsorship but most recruits, or more usually their parents, had to pay their own fares and training expenses. From 1955 the British government offered loans for help with travel but recruits had to pay these back at a certain amount per week.

The response

Nurses and ancillary workers were recruited throughout the British Commonwealth and from Ireland. But during the early years, most came from the Caribbean. Until 1962 Commonwealth citizens had unrestricted entry to Britain. Exact figures are not known, but between 1948–69 thousands of nurses, trainees and other ancillary workers arrived in Britain to work in the health service. By 1954 more than 3,000 Caribbean women were training in British hospitals; by 1959 official statistics showed 6,365 colonial nursing students in Britain. In 1968, according to the trade union Unison, there were 6,450 West Indian trainees in British hospitals.

In 1969 the *Nursing Times* stated that some 300–600 fully trained Commonwealth nurses arrived in Britain every year between 1964–67, but thousands more came to be trained as nurses or midwives. In 1959–60 some 5,850 trainee nurses and midwives arrived in Britain from overseas. In 1966–67 the figure was 16,745. Of these, nearly 75 per cent were from the Caribbean.

Caribbean background

Most nurses and ancillary workers came from Barbados, Jamaica and Trinidad & Tobago. They also came from other islands, including St Lucia and St Vincent, and from British Guiana.

The women and men who left the Caribbean to work in the NHS were from a variety of social and economic backgrounds. Most were in their late teens or early twenties; some were as young as 15 when they left their homes to make the 6,450-km (4,000-mile) journey to Britain. Many came from homes in which one family member had some experience of medicine: a father who was a pharmacist or an aunt who had been a nurse. Many had wanted to be nurses from childhood. Some had left school when they were 14 or 15 but many candidates had gone through secondary school and had O levels and A levels. Some had already done some medical training in the Caribbean or had acquired work experience. Some West Indian doctors had qualified in the Caribbean; others were looking to complete their training in places like Edinburgh or London.

IMMIGRATION ACTS
- 1948 British Nationalities Act gave British citizenship to all Commonwealth citizens. Peoples of the Commonwealth could enter Britain freely as British citizens.
- 1962 Commonwealth Immigrants Act imposed restrictions and ended automatic right of entry. The only categories of Commonwealth citizens able to enter Britain were holders of employment vouchers issued by the Ministry of Labour, students, members of the armed forces, and entrants who could demonstrate an ability to support themselves.

Stocking the dressing trolley, Mile End Hospital, c1970 (Royal London Hospital Archives: ME/P/12)

Mother country

There was a long tradition of people leaving the West Indies for work. Until the end of World War Two, most went to the United States. In 1952 America restricted immigration. West Indians therefore chose to come to Britain, many responding to the British government's call for more workers and expecting a warm welcome.

The first postwar Caribbean immigrants arrived in 1948 on board the *SS Empire Windrush*, which brought 492 Jamaicans to Britain. From then on, increasing numbers of people left the Caribbean to work in Britain not just in the new health service but also in transport, construction and other industries that were desperately in need of workers to rebuild postwar Britain.

For many Caribbeans, Britain was seen as the mother country. Schooling and learning in the West Indies were modelled on English lines and English was the spoken language. Caribbeans also shared many cultural interests with the British. West Indians held British passports and were British subjects, with automatic right of entry, at least until the law changed in 1962.

Progressing medical careers

For those who wanted to work as doctors, nurses and healthcare professionals, there were limited opportunities in the Caribbean. It was difficult to obtain high-level qualifications and there was little chance of promotion. White British expatriates held the senior nursing and other professional positions. Britain offered the opportunity of achieving high-level qualifications, work experience and job satisfaction. Many were encouraged by their families to make the move. Most of those who came in the early years intended to return to the Caribbean once they had gained qualifications and experience, both passports to good jobs in the West Indies.

First impressions

Between 1948–69, thousands of women and men left the West Indies to take up jobs in the British health service. They travelled by plane or by ship, on journeys that could take two to three weeks. Some had applied for jobs in advance and already had places in specific hospitals; others were posted to hospitals anywhere in the United Kingdom when they arrived. Some came to join relatives

© *Photo by Douglas Miller/Keystone/Getty Images*

already in Britain and applied for jobs when they arrived.

First impressions of Britain were often daunting. After the sunshine of the Caribbean, newcomers found the cold climate and grey drabness of Britain shocking. Terraced houses, coal fires and smoking chimneys were all new experiences. Everything was different, including the food, which seemed bland and tasteless. Friends or relatives sometimes met the new arrivals from the train. During the 1950s the British Council provided care and help for students and student nurses and sometimes a matron from the hospital might welcome new arrivals at the railway station. Often, however, new arrivals had to make their own way to the hospital, usually dressed in clothing unsuitable for the cold British weather.

Life in Britain was very different from the Caribbean. Newcomers were surprised to see white people sweeping the street, carrying luggage or

© Photo by Haywood Magee/Picture Post/Getty Images

A young girl leaning on her luggage at Victoria Station, London, 9 June 1956

"WHAT THEY DIDN'T TELL YOU TO EXPECT WAS THE AMOUNT OF PREJUDICES AND DISCRIMINATION THAT YOU ENCOUNTERED"
Denzil Nurse

doing other menial work, something that was unheard of in the Caribbean. Many felt homesick and isolated. Some, like Daisy Anson who worked as a cook in the Nottingham City Hospital in the late 1950s, found they were "the only black one there"; others, like Joyce Bleasdille-Lumsden who came to Britain from Grenada in 1960, found there were other black nurses in Stoke Mandeville Hospital where she was placed. Colonial workers supported each other, helping to overcome the strangeness of the new country. Despite the unfamiliarity, most newcomers were excited at being in Britain and thrilled by the opportunities to work in the NHS.

Hard work and disappointment
Expectations were high but there were

disappointments. Many trainee nurses wanted and had expected to go into general nursing but most were placed in psychiatric wards or hospitals for the elderly and chronically sick, areas of nursing that were not popular with white nurses. Caribbean nurses, who had not been trained in these fields before, found themselves working with violent and challenging behaviour. Many became very skilled in psychiatric nursing.

Training was hard and again Caribbean recruits found things were not as expected. Nurse training operated on two levels: the 'pupil' or State Enrolled Nurse (SEN) qualification, which was not recognised in the Caribbean, and the more advanced 'staff' or State Registered Nurse (SRN) training, which included ward management and was needed for progression.

Caribbean trainees were almost invariably placed on SEN training, even when they had the necessary qualifications for SRN and had been told they would go onto SRN courses. Some recruits challenged the decision but were usually persuaded to take up SEN training before progressing to SRN training, so adding two or more years to their training. Evidence shows that while Caribbean nurses failed to be accepted onto SRN training, English young women without qualifications were. Most Caribbean recruits had little doubt that the system was biased in favour of white nurses and that they had to take SEN because they were black.

Trainees lived in nurses' homes attached to

their hospitals. Accommodation was basic and there were strict rules. Bells woke them early in the morning and they had to be back in the home by 10pm. If they stayed out late, they were put on report. It was assumed that black nurses were much less likely to complain about conditions than their white colleagues.

Trainee nurses worked long hours for low pay. T Anderson, who came from Jamaica in 1952, remembers working for 48 hours a week, in shifts, with only alternate weekends off. Discipline was strict and wards were run on military lines. Matrons had absolute authority. For the first few weeks or months, Caribbean nurses were put to all the menial duties, helping with meals, emptying bedpans and cleaning. Many new recruits did not consider this real nursing. Overseas recruits found themselves on regular night shifts and doing menial tasks rather than the nursing duties they had expected. Despite 'pupil' status they were often left alone, and many developed back trouble from lifting patients.

Discrimination
In general Caribbean nurses and ancillary workers had good relationships with their colleagues and patients. They worked hard and were respected for their commitment and skills. But racial prejudice and discrimination existed inside hospitals and out. Some patients objected to being handled and nursed by black nurses. Senior staff blocked

Caribbean workers from going onto higher qualifications, more senior positions or into specialist areas of care. Caribbeans trying to move into specialisms were often told that such work was not for black people. During the 1950s and 1960s, many Caribbeans encountered the notorious sign 'No Dogs, No Blacks, No Irish' when they looked for lodgings. Some bought their own property but had to fight for the right to get a loan.

Barriers to promotion

It was difficult for Caribbean and other black workers to achieve promotion within the NHS. Dr Stanley Moonsawmy, who came to England from Guyana in 1956, worked as a hospital doctor but, being unable to achieve registrar grade, went into general practice, because he "had reached what was regarded in those days as the ceiling for non-white doctors." In 1969 the *Nursing Times* insisted that the position of overseas nurses should be looked into, and drew attention to the fact that only five per cent of overseas-born nurses were reaching the upper fifth of the nursing profession, despite the fact that they made up such a large proportion of all nurses working in Britain. Time and time again Caribbean and other minority ethnic workers found their progression barred by misconceptions and prejudice.

Some Caribbean workers joined trade unions or the Royal College of Nursing to highlight issues of racism, but not many did so during the 1950s and 1960s. At that stage nursing was still seen as too respectable a profession for union membership to be appropriate. The TUC's official policy was to cooperate with the recruitment of overseas workers and to condemn all forms of racial prejudice by government, employers or workers. However this did not always manifest itself in practice. In 1956, for instance, a local union branch opposed the employment of 'coloured nurses' at Storthes Mental Hospital. Despite its official policy, the TUC in those years was also concerned that the employment of overseas labour should not damage the situation of white workers. It was not until the mid-1960s and 1970s that anti-racist legislation was introduced and became part of the political agenda. In the 1980s some black and minority ethnic nurses began setting up black sections in what were then NUPE and NALGO.

Asian recruitment

By 1960 the NHS was facing another crisis – this time a serious shortage of doctors. British-born doctors were leaving the NHS in droves, emigrating to Canada, the United States, Australia and New Zealand in search of better-paid prospects. Once again, the NHS called on overseas sources to fill the vacancies, this time focusing on the Indian subcontinent. During the 1960s and 1970s, thousands of doctors emigrated from India, Pakistan, Bangladesh and Sri Lanka to work in the NHS, which they were told offered enormous possibilities. Like their Caribbean colleagues, Asian doctors experienced considerable racism and discrimination and were undervalued at the time. Many worked as GPs in run-down inner city practices, while their white counterparts went abroad or into wealthier communities.

Trailblazers

Some 70 per cent of the first generation of Caribbean nurses, doctors and ancillary workers who joined the NHS during its first 21 years did not return to the Caribbean. They remained in Britain because of family commitments, familiarity with their new homeland and dedication to their work. They wanted to stay. Caribbean nurses and ancillary workers found their own ways of overcoming prejudice and discrimination. Using determination and initiative – and sometimes encouraged by work colleagues, friendly matrons or other senior staff – they overcame the barriers, improved their situation and provided an invaluable contribution to the NHS. They pursued further training when opportunities arose, switched hospitals and went on to become matrons, midwives, health visitors and other more specialist practitioners, making such moves possible for the second-generation black and ethnic minority workers who followed. Although only a small percentage did so, some broke

Nurses' practical classroom, Mile End Hospital, c1960s (Royal London Hospital Archives: ME/P/19)

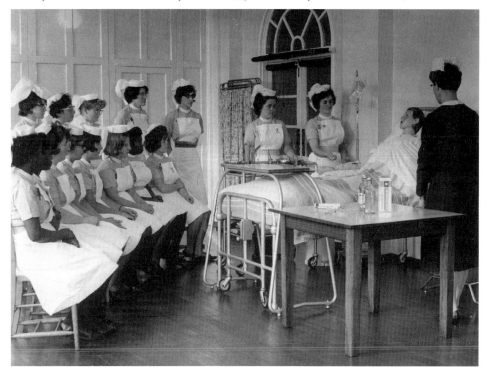

through to become nursing directors and to hold senior positions.

First-generation Caribbean health workers were trailblazers. As Britain became an increasingly multi-ethnic and multiracial society, many Caribbean health professionals developed a particular interest in working with and helping black and minority ethnic groups. It was they who highlighted and raised awareness of ethnic health issues such as sickle-cell anaemia and thalassaemia, which were being overlooked by a white-dominated health service. They set up support groups and focused attention on the need for more provision within the NHS. Some also made major contribution to the developments of health services in the Caribbean.

A vital role

In 1961 Norman Pannel MP wrote to Enoch Powell, then Minister of Health, stating, 'hospitals could not carry on without coloured immigrant nurses.' In 1969 the *Nursing Times* stated that they played a 'vital role in keeping British hospitals operating.' Caribbean and other overseas nurses, midwives, and ancillary workers made up 25–33 per cent of the NHS staff in its first 21 years; the service would not have functioned without them. The decline in infant mortality alone — to 4.9 per 1,000 live births in 2004 — stands as testament.

The NHS has been slow to recognise their contribution and to acknowledge the discrimination and barriers faced by black and ethnic minority health workers. Recent signs indicate that things are changing for the better. In 1994 the Mary Seacole Leadership Awards were set up to acknowledge the contribution made to the nation's health by black and minority ethnic professionals. In 1998, on the 50th anniversary of the NHS, Baroness Jay acknowledged the work of black and minority ethnic workers, pointing out that they remain essential to ensure that the NHS is responsive to the needs of multi-ethnic Britain. In 2000 the NHS published The Vital Connection: An Equalities Framework for the NHS, and in 2003 a new national forum was launched to promote the development of black and minority ethnic leadership in the health service. In 2004 Sir Nigel Crisp launched a Leadership and Race Equality Action Plan for the NHS, and at the same time the Race for Health programme was set up to transform services and the workplace for black and minority ethnic individuals for the better.

The first generation of Caribbean workers in the NHS chose to come to Britain and they are proud of their achievements. The NHS needs black and ethnic minority health professionals to continue its work of treating the nation's health and to meet the needs of a multi-ethnic society. Many of the first generation Caribbean health professionals are still working today to encourage their successors to take up the challenge.

Timeline

1945

1950

1945
World War Two ends. Labour Party comes to power with programme of social reform. After six years of war, Britain needs to rebuild its economy and repair war damage to schools, hospitals, factories and homes. To do this, Britain needs more workers.

1946
The National Health Service Bill becomes law. The service will provide free healthcare for all, irrespective of a person's ability to pay. Taxation and national insurance will fund the new service, which will be controlled by the government. There is a need for at least 42,000 more hospital staff in the new health service.

1948
The *SS Empire Windrush* arrives in Britain from Jamaica. It marks the start of postwar mass migration from the Caribbean. The British Nationalities Act gives British citizenship to all members of the Commonwealth, who have automatic right to live and work in Britain. The National Health Service is launched on 5 July. One of its priorities is to recruit more staff for hospitals. Nursing recruits and ancillary workers begin arriving in Britain from the Caribbean; greater numbers will arrive in the 1950s and 1960s.

1949
Recruitment for nursing staff and ancillary workers takes place in Britain and overseas. Advertisements appear in the nursing press and in Caribbean newspapers such as the *Barbados Advocate* and *Barbados Beacon*. Senior nursing professionals go to the Caribbean to recruit for staff. In Britain, clothes rationing ends.

1950
General election returns Labour government. Some 5,000 black Commonwealth citizens have arrived in Britain since 1948 to work or join relatives. As British citizens, they expect a warm welcome but most encounter racial discrimination. David Pitt sets up medical practice, London. Korean War begins (ends 1953).

1951
Festival of Britain in London celebrates modern British inventions and design. NHS costs about £358 million annually, far higher than expected. Aneurin Bevan, architect of the NHS, resigns from the cabinet in protest against proposed health charges. Conservatives win general election.

1952
USA passes the McCarran–Walter Act, which restricts Caribbean emigration to the United States. Caribbean migrants look to Britain for work and career opportunities unavailable in the Caribbean. NHS introduces prescription charges of one shilling (5p) and a flat fee of £1 for ordinary dental treatment.

© Courtesy of Imperial War Museum

A group of West Indian women recruited to join the ATS, waiting for transport to take them to their training camp

Many rivers to cross

1953

Coronation of Queen Elizabeth II takes place in London. More than 300,000 new homes are built in Britain. The first successful open heart surgery takes place in the USA. Francis Crick and James Watson announce the discovery of the double helix structure of DNA, the basic material of heredity.

Lord David Pitt (left, bottom row)

1954

Some 10,000 Caribbean immigrants arrive in Britain. The *Barbados Advocate* reports that some landladies and lodging houses are refusing to accept 'coloured colonials'. Food rationing ends in Britain. Polio vaccine is tested in the USA. 'Rock'n'roll' becomes popular.

1955

Conservatives win general election. Commercial television begins in Britain. Selection committees are set up in the Caribbean to choose nursing recruits for NHS hospitals. British government offers some financial help but most recruits fund themselves. About 3,000 colonial women are training in NHS hospitals. Most black recruits are forced to take up SEN training rather than SRN. SEN 'pupil' nurses wear check uniforms as opposed to the starched green uniforms of SRN nurses. Civil rights campaigners in the USA boycott segregated buses.

1956

Guillebaud Committee reports on the NHS and states that no reforms are necessary. Britain's first large-scale nuclear power station opens, Calder Hall. About 26,400 West Indians arrive in Britain. London Transport begins to recruit for workers from Barbados; direct recruitment continues until 1970. Storthes Mental Hospital refuses to employ 'coloured nurses'. A few activists, including David Pitt, defend growing black population against racial discrimination.

1957

Britain explodes its first thermonuclear bomb. The Soviet Union (now Russia) launches Sputnik I and II into space orbit. Oral polio vaccine is produced. In Britain, postwar recovery is booming. Prime Minister Harold Macmillan tells the British public: "you've never had it so good." Guyana-born Cy Grant sings the news calypso style on BBC TV programme *Tonight*.

Cy Grant

1958

Racial tensions increase in Britain. Whites attack black residents in Nottingham and west London, sparking so-called race riots. Civil liberty groups denounce the atmosphere of violence. There are increasing calls for immigration controls.

Claudia Jones

© *Courtesy of Lambeth Archives*

Trinidadian Claudia Jones founds *West Indian Gazette* to promote equal rights for black community. West Indian Standing Conference (WISC) forms to promote interests of Afro-Caribbean community in Britain. Campaign for Nuclear Disarmament (CND) is formed. Thousands march from London to the nuclear base in Aldermaston to protest against nuclear weapons. Nurses' working week is reduced from 48 hours to 44.

1960

1959
About 10 million British households own televisions. General election returns Conservative government with big majority. Nurses receive a 12 per cent pay increase; their pay remains far behind those of teachers and other comparable professionals. Some 20,400 West Indians move to Britain. Afro-Asian West Indian Nurses Association forms but is short-lived. David Pitt stands for parliament, the first black Caribbean to do so, but fails to gain seat.

1961
Enoch Powell, Minister of Health, announces an 11 per cent increase in costs of NHS. He doubles prescription and other charges. The NHS begins recruiting doctors from India and Pakistan. There are about 500,000 Caribbean and South Asian people in Britain – about one per cent of the population. Pay freeze introduced. Oral contraceptive – the pill – becomes available. Soviet cosmonaut Yuri Gagarin becomes first man in space. Berlin Wall completed.

1962
Commonwealth Immigrants Act ends open access for Commonwealth citizens. Entry restricted to those who have been issued with employment vouchers, or those who can support themselves without working. Would-be nurses need to have employment vouchers. Labour opposition leader, Hugh Gaitskell, calls the act "a plain anti-colour measure". Jamaica and Trinidad & Tobago gain independence. Royal College of Physicians confirms links between smoking, cancer and heart disease. SEN nurses earn about £2 per week. Nurses campaign for more pay.

1963
Enoch Powell announces a 10-year plan of community care under an expanding NHS. Numbers of West Indian arrivals in Britain fall to an average of less than 14,000 a year. Inquiry into slum landlords, particularly Rachman in Notting Hill who lets sub-standard housing at high prices to West Indians. Measles vaccine produced. President Kennedy assassinated in Dallas, Texas. Valentina Tereshkova becomes first woman in space. Rachel Carson's *The Silent Spring* highlights dangers of chemical pesticides. Surgeons in Leeds perform successful kidney transplant.

1964
A Labour government is elected under Harold Wilson. Peter Griffiths, Conservative MP, is elected in Smethwick on a racist ticket. Guyana-born Daphne Steele becomes Britain's first black matron, having risen through the ranks as a midwife at St Winifred's Hospital, West Yorkshire. Beatlemania sweeps Britain and USA.

FACE THE FACTS

IF YOU DESIRE A **COLOURED** FOR YOUR NEIGHBOUR

VOTE LABOUR

IF YOU ARE ALREADY BURDENED WITH ONE

VOTE TORY

The Conservatives once in Office, will bring up to date the Ministry of Repatriation, to Speed up the return of home-going and expelled immigrants.

1965
Race Relations Act outlaws discrimination in public places and sets up Race Relations Board to investigate complaints of unlawful discrimination. Government restricts spending on housing, schools and hospitals. White Paper on Commonwealth immigration proposes annual limit of 8,500 employment vouchers a year, to be issued mainly to skilled/professional workers. Campaign Against Racial Discrimination (CARD) founded; David Pitt becomes first chair. Anti-Vietnam war demonstrations in USA. Mini-skirts fashionable.

1966
General election returns Labour government. Wages freeze in Britain. British Guiana gains independence as Guyana. Barbados becomes independent within Commonwealth. London Transport recruits workers from Trinidad & Tobago. German measles vaccine developed. Black Panthers form, USA.

Many rivers to cross

1967 Norwell Roberts becomes first black British police officer

1968 Martin Luther King is assassinated

1970

1967

National Front forms. Abortion Act legalises abortion. Sexual Offences Act decriminalises homosexual acts between consenting adults. Growing protests in UK and US against Vietnam War. First heart transplant operation takes place, South Africa. In Britain, health improvements mean deaths from TB have dropped to about 2,000 a year from about 23,000 a year in 1948. Coronary bypass operation is developed. Mammography (X-ray technique for detecting breast cancer) is developed. Six-Day War, Israel.

1968

Commonwealth Immigrants Act imposes further controls on immigration. Enoch Powell makes notorious 'rivers of blood' speech attacking black and Asian immigration. Race Relations Act widens anti discrimination to include housing, employment and provision of goods and services; Community Relations Commission (CRC) set up. Students rebel in Paris, London, USA. Violence flares in Northern Ireland, sparking off years of conflict. Civil Rights leader Martin Luther King is assassinated, USA.

1969

British government introduces white paper In Place of Strife to deal with growing union unrest but it is soon abandoned. Enoch Powell calls for repatriation of black immigrants. Death penalty abolished. Jimmy Cliff releases 'Wonderful World, Beautiful People', a major reggae hit. Voting age lowered to 18. Women workers at Ford plant strike for equal pay. Black and minority ethnic nurses now make up about 25 per cent of NHS hospital staff. American astronauts, Neil Armstrong and Buzz Aldrin become first men to land on moon. Gay rights movement begins, USA.

1970

Public sector workers strike for better pay. General election returns Conservative government under Ted Heath. Royal College of Nurses conduct pay campaign: admit SENs and pupil nurses. Equal Pay Bill introduced: it becomes law in 1975.

1971

Immigration Act establishes 'partiality': right of immigration restricted to those whose parents or grandparents were born in the UK. Act virtually ends immigration from the Caribbean. Decimal currency introduced. Industrial Relations Bill becomes law. Coronary artery by-pass surgery developed. First national Women's Liberation Movement demonstration takes place in London. Some 1,500,000 Caribbean and South Asians are living in Britain, about three per cent of the population. Ska music becomes popular with white youth.

1972

Ancillary nursing staff strike for better pay and conditions: the 'raise the roof' campaign. Black and minority ethnic nurses involve themselves in strike action. Bloody Sunday (30 January): British troops kill 13 demonstrators in Derry, Northern Ireland. Industrial militancy increases: miners and dockers strike.

1974

General election results in a Labour minority government. NHS undergoes the most far-reaching reorganisation since its foundation. A three-tiered administration structure is introduced with area health authorities, regional health authorities, and a central department. Caribbean migration to Britain effectively ends. Immigration from India, Pakistan and Bangladesh continues, but at reduced rate.

CHARING CROSS   HOSPITAL GROUP

HARROW HOSPITAL

Certificate of Training

TESTIFYING THAT

Mrs. Lena Emily Hunt, née Herelle

commenced her Training as a Student Nurse on the
twelfth day of **February, 1950**
in the Charing Cross Hospital Group Training School of
Nursing, and received the major part of this training at
the Harrow Hospital. She has satisfactorily passed the
required examinations and has completed the term of
2½ years training.

Signed this **13th** day of **August 1952**

A. H. ....

Chairman of the House Committee

N. Jewell F.R.C.S.I. M.D.

W. McK. H. McCullagh F.R.C.O.G. ⎫ Examiners

E. Martin.

Matron

Chapter 1
Biographical Notes

More than 30 people were interviewed for this book. Each played a vital role in the early years of the NHS. Their stories have helped to shape the contents of this book and enable us to see what life was like for Caribbean health practitioners in the first twenty or so years of the NHS. There is a brief biography of each interviewee on the following pages.

Photographs by Abigail Bernard

Lena Hunt's certificate of training, 1950

Nurses

>>>>>>>>>>>>>>>

Tryphena Anderson

Tryphena Anderson was born in Jamaica. She attended a Church of England school. Aged 19 she left Jamaica for England in December 1952, just a week after leaving school. She travelled by boat on the *HMS Franconia* from New York to Liverpool. She did her nurse training at Nottingham General Hospital, working as a junior nurse. She went on to do psychiatric nursing at the Coppice Hospital, Nottingham. In the early 1960s she did postgraduate training and in 1966 qualified as a midwife. That year too she became the first black person to receive a bursary to train as a health visitor. In 1988 she bought a nursing home, which she ran until 2002.

Tryphena Anderson, 2005

Joyce Bleasdille-Lumsden

Joyce Bleasdille-Lumsden was born in Grenada. She attended St David's RC School and the Anglican School. In 1952 she left school, aged 15. She did voluntary work in hospitals, and worked as a probationer before leaving Grenada for England in 1960. She travelled to England by ship. She trained at Tynesdale General Hospital, Buckinghamshire, one of only five black nurses from the Caribbean. In 1962 she transferred to Colindale. She went on to qualify as a midwife at Luton Maternity in 1967. She worked as a ward sister until 1974 and from then until 1993 worked as a community sister. Now retired, she remains active fundraising for community projects in the UK and Grenada.

Joyce Bleasdille-Lumsden, 2005

Muriel Bussue

Muriel Bussue was born in St Kitts. She left school when she was 16 and worked as a seamstress. In 1956 her husband left for England to find work. Two years later, when she was in her mid-20s, she and her children travelled to England by ship to join him. Later she applied to train as a nurse and, despite some initial resistance from her husband, managed to combine nursing with parenting. She worked as a nurse in the NHS for 33 years. Now retired, she continues to do voluntary work in the community. Two of her children have followed her into the medical profession.

Muriel Bussue, 2005

Gloria Falode

Gloria Falode was born in Trinidad. She attended a Catholic convent school and, from the age of 10, the Providence Intermediate Girls School. She achieved her school certificate. In 1960, aged 23, she sailed to England. She trained as a nurse in a psychiatric hospital in Nottingham. In 1962 she moved on to the Royal Homeopathic Hospital in London. She qualified as a State Registered Nurse in 1965. She worked as a staff nurse in Loughborough, later qualifying as a midwife. From 1968–74 she worked as a staff nurse at Queen Mary's Hospital, Roehampton. She retired in 1994, having worked as a nursing officer for some years. She remains active, assessing a new generation of nursing students.

Gloria Falode passing exams, January 2005

Louise Garvey

Louise Garvey was born in Jamaica. She attended a church school and passed her national exams. In 1957, when she was 15, she came to England by plane. Her mother was already in England. Initially, Louse Garvey worked in a cotton factory. Then, aged 17, she started training as a cadet nurse at Congleton Hospital, Cheshire. She qualified as a State Registered Nurse, progressing to the position of sister. She has actively promoted equality in the health sector and highlighted the situation of black nurses in a booklet, *Nursing Lives of Black Nurses in Nottingham*. She still serves on a hospital panel in Nottingham.

Louise Garvey, 2005

Lena Hunt

Lena Hunt was born in St Kitts and educated at the Senior Girls High School. She left school when she was 16. In 1948, aged 18, she came to England by ship to train as a nurse at Redhill Hospital, Surrey. Once qualified, she held various nursing posts, working in orthopaedic wards and outpatient departments. She retired from nursing in 1992. Her two daughters have both followed her into nursing.

Staff nurse Mrs Lena Hunt with her father, George Herelle

Dr Nola Ishmael OBE

Dr Nola Ishmael was born in Barbados. She attended Black Bess Mixed School and the Community High School in Bridgetown. She left school aged 15 with O levels. In 1963, aged 20, she arrived in England by plane. She trained as a nurse, qualified at the Whittington Hospital, London, and took up a staff nursing post, working in a high-dependency ward. She became a night sister and in 1977 qualified as a health visitor. In 1987 she achieved the post of assistant director of nursing, subsequently becoming director of nursing in Greenwich. In 1995 she became the first black professional private secretary to the Chief Nurse of England. In 2000 she was awarded an OBE. She retired in 2003 but continues to work part-time at the Department of Health, mentoring and coaching the next generation of BME nurses.

Dr Nola Ishmael, 2005

Margaret Knight

Margaret Knight was born in Barbados. She came to England in 1945, at the end of World War Two. She attended school in Bournemouth until 1948, returned to Barbados for a year, then came back to England in 1949. In 1950 she began training as a nurse at King's College Hospital, London, but was unable to complete her training because of illness. She later worked as an orderly in occupational therapy and did administrative work in medical records.

Margaret Knight, King's College Hospital during nurse training, 1949

Lucy Martin-Burnham

Lucy Martin-Burnham was born in Jamaica. She attended Park Hill School. In 1951, aged 19, she sailed to England. She trained as a nurse in Amersham General Hospital, Buckinghamshire. In 1956 she qualified as a midwife and a year later became a health visitor. In 1959 she returned to Jamaica for two years, working as a public health visitor. She returned to England and from 1962–96 worked for Berkshire County Council as a health visitor organising key projects, including the first home-help service, the first childminding service, the first playgroup and the first invitation to fathers to attend the birth of their children.

Lucy Martin-Burnham, 2005

Denzil Nurse

Denzil Nurse was born in Barbados. He attended Mount Tabor Primary School and then went onto secondary school. He left before taking his exams, intending to apply to join the British Air Force. Deemed too young he opted for nursing and in 1963, aged 19, travelled to Britain. He studied nursing at the Stanley Royd Hospital in Yorkshire. He specialised in psychiatric nursing, working as a staff nurse for 23 years. In 1986 he moved into community development, working with the Afro-Caribbean community in Huddersfield and developing a range of health and social care projects. A few years ago he visited Gambia and 'adopted' an African village, where he has set up community projects.

Denzil Nurse, 2005

Lynette Richards-Murray

Lynette Richards-Murray was born in Guyana. After leaving school, she worked as a civil servant for two years. In 1959, when she was 20, she came over to England by ship. She trained as a nurse in Taunton, qualified and became a staff nurse. She went on to become a midwife. In 1973 she obtained her first nursing office post, in Greenwich, then worked her way up to became director of nursing in South London in 1977. She retired in 1992 and decided to focus on health needs in Guyana. She continues to work with the Association of Guyanese Nurses and Allied Professionals (AGNAP) and has been instrumental in setting up a service for the deaf in Guyana.

Lynette Richards-Murray, 2005

Sherlene Rudder MBE

Sherlene Rudder was born in Barbados. In 1964, when she was 18, she travelled to England by plane, to start her training at Pembury Hospital, Kent. She qualified as a State Registered Nurse in 1967. She went on to train in midwifery and, in 1971, health visiting. She worked as a health visitor for 16 years. In 1979 she was instrumental in setting up the Sickle-Cell Society in Harlesden. She became a genetic counsellor in 1988, working with a variety of genetic conditions as well as sickle cell. In 1995 she was awarded an MBE for her work in the community. She remains active in voluntary work, counselling families with genetic conditions.

Sherlene Rudder, 2005

Dr Neslyn Watson-Druée OBE

Dr Neslyn Watson-Druée was born in Jamaica. In 1969, aged 19, she travelled by plane to England to train as a nurse. She trained in Tunbridge Wells. In 1973 she transferred to Kingston-upon-Thames Hospital where she studied and qualified as a midwife. She went on to become a health visitor and subsequently a lecturer. In 1988 she set up her own business: career development company for ethnic minorities, which she continues today. She currently leads the Kingston Primary Care NHS Trust.

Neslyn Watson-Druée MBE, 2005

Allied Health Professionals, Auxiliaries and Maintenance

>>>>>>>>>>>>>

Daisy V V Anson

Daisy V V Anson was born in Jamaica. She attended Campbell Castle Primary School but did not go onto high school. She left school aged 15. In 1956 she came to England, travelling on board ship. She went to Nottingham where she worked in the Sherwood Hospital laundry department and later went into hospital catering, cooking for up to 300 people. In 1975 she returned to the Caribbean.

Daisy V V Anson, 2005

Nelson Auguste

Nelson Auguste was born in St Lucia. He left school aged 16 and worked in a sugar cane factory. In 1960, aged 20, he left St Lucia for England. He worked in factories, on building sites and as a gravedigger. In 1972 he began work as a general porter in the National Heart Hospital, London. He subsequently became a theatre porter and ultimately supervisor. He was nominated shop steward of his union and was active defending workers' rights. He retired in 1994 and is currently treasurer for the St Lucia Association.

Nelson Auguste, 2005

Olivine Benjamin

Olivine Benjamin was born in Jamaica, where she attended Catholic school. In 1965, when she was 16, she travelled to England by plane. She worked in a factory for about two years. When she was 18, she obtained a job as a nursing auxiliary in the Northern General Hospital. She retired in 2000, having worked in the NHS for 34 years.

Olivine Benjamin, 2005

Leila Ghartey

Leila Ghartey was born in Guyana. She attended school until the age of 18. After leaving school, she worked in a medical laboratory attached to the main hospital in Georgetown. In 1961, aged 22, she travelled to England by plane to study at the Lister Institute of Preventative Medicine. In 1968 she began training as a physiotherapist, one of the few Caribbean people in the profession at that time. She worked as a physiotherapist in various hospitals, becoming a senior physiotherapist in 1992. She retired in 2004.

Leila Ghartey, 2005

Derek Harty

Derek Harty was born in Jamaica. He attended primary and secondary schools. After leaving school he worked in Kingston Public Hospital as a laboratory technician. In 1965, aged 23, he left Jamaica for England, travelling by plane. He obtained a job as a junior technician in the NHS and went on to pursue further academic qualifications. He became a registered laboratory scientist and in 1973 became a fellow of biomedical sciences. He is currently technical manager for the biochemistry department at Whipps Cross Hospital, London.

Derek Harty, 2005

Caswell Jeffrey

Caswell Jeffrey was born in Jamaica. He left school aged 16 and was interested in woodwork. He trained and qualified as a carpenter. In 1960 he emigrated to England, travelling by ship. He gained a position as a carpenter at the General Hospital, Birmingham, where he worked for more than 30 years. In 1988 his union, UCATT, appointed him health and safety representative. He retired in 1992.

Caswell Jeffrey, 2005

Many rivers to cross

Erena Kydd

Erena Kydd was born in St Vincent and went to school in Georgetown. In 1959, aged 22 and seeking adventure, she travelled to England by boat. She started work as an auxiliary at Queen Elizabeth Hospital, Birmingham. Despite many difficulties and challenges, she remained committed to the health service until her retirement in 1992. She has been active in community work and as a school governor. She continues to do voluntary work with the blind.

Erena Kydd, 2005

Thelma Lewis

Thelma Lewis was born in Guyana. She attended primary and secondary school, gaining her senior Cambridge certificate. She trained and worked as a nurse in Guyana. In 1955, aged 22, she came over to England by boat, on the *SS Colombie*, to work in Houghton Hospital, Epsom. Initially she worked as a nurse in mental health. In 1956 she switched to medical technology, qualifying and working as a laboratory technician at St George's Hospital until 1968. She later specialised in haematology. She is now retired but is closely connected to the Roman Catholic Church and does voluntary work in St Vincent.

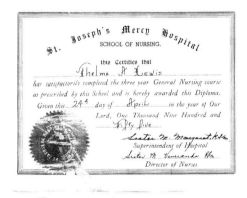

Thelma Lewis's nursing certificate from St Joseph's Mercy Hospital, Guyana

Siburnie Ramharry

Siburnie Ramharry was born in Guyana. After leaving high school, she worked as a laboratory assistant. In 1962, aged 19, she left Guyana for Scotland to train as a dietician. She travelled by plane. She trained in Edinburgh and qualified in 1966. She became a basic grade dietician, and later a nutritionist, building up experience in the UK and the Caribbean. In 1980 she became dietetic manager with Liverpool Health Authority and in 1988 became manager of the Charing Cross and Westminster group of hospitals. Since 1993 she has been a senior primary care dietician with East Pembridge Mid-Surrey Primary Care Trust.

Siburnie Ramharry, 2005

Inez Stewart

Inez Stewart was born in Jamaica. She left school when she was 15. In 1960, aged 21, she came to England by plane. Initially she worked in a factory in Sheffield but in 1962 she took a hospital job in the Northern General Hospital, working in the dining room. She was the only Caribbean worker. Subsequently she became a nursing auxiliary.

Inez Stuart, 2005

Hazel Watson

Hazel Watson was born in Barbados. She left school when she was 14. She applied to various hospitals in England and in 1957, aged 16, travelled to England by boat on a government recruitment scheme. She worked as a housekeeper and supervisor in Abbots Langley Hospital, Hertfordshire, and later at Guy's Hospital, London. She retired in 1998. She is currently involved with a youth community group.

Hazel Watson (centre), 2005

Elizabeth Yates

Elizabeth Yates was born in Guyana. She attended high school, took A levels and qualified as a geography teacher. In 1962, aged 19, she travelled to England by plane to train as an occupational therapist. She trained at the London School of Occupational Therapists, the only Caribbean person in the college at that time. She qualified in 1965 and started her first clinical appointment. In 1970 she took a full-time post as occupational therapist at the Royal National Orthopaedic Hospital at Great Portland Street. In 1972 she was appointed head occupational therapist at the Royal Northern Hospital, becoming the first black person to achieve that level of post. She retired in 1993 but currently works on the steering group with Neslyn Watson-Druée on a career development programme for occupational therapists.

Elizabeth Yates, 2004

Doctors and Dentists

>>>>>>>>>>>>>>>

Dr Eddie Adams

Dr Eddie Adams was born in Guyana. He attended school in Georgetown, obtaining the Cambridge overseas certificate. In 1953, aged 27, he travelled to England on the *SS Colombie*. He was awarded a grant to study medicine at King's College, London and qualified as a surgeon. His first job in the NHS was at King's College Hospital in 1964. He joined Lambeth Hospital as a surgeon and was later attached to St Thomas's. He worked as a surgeon in major hospitals across London. In 1977 he opened his own practice in Streatham, London.

Dr Eddie Adams, 2005

Dr Victor Eastmond

Dr Victor Eastmond was born in Barbados. He achieved A levels at school and in 1964, aged 19, emigrated to Britain, having applied to work with London Transport. He travelled by plane. He worked as a guard with London Transport for a year, then switched career to dentistry, a long-held ambition. He studied radiography at the Royal Free Hospital, Hampstead. He completed his training in 1969, before going freelance within the NHS. In 1970, aged 25, he gained a place at the Royal Dental Hospital, London. In 1975 he set up his own dental practice. In 1979 he went back to Barbados, where he now runs a successful dental practice.

Dr Eastmond, 2005

Dr Franklyn Jacobs

Dr Franklyn Jacobs was born in St Vincent. He attended primary and secondary school and went to the University of the West Indies to study medicine. He left university in 1968 and worked as a doctor in Trinidad. In 1974 he travelled to Britain to obtain further training in anaesthetics. In 1977 he went into general practice within the NHS, working in a predominantly Greek community in North London. Since 1982 he has run his own general practice. Dr Jacobs is one of the founders of the African Caribbean Medical Society (together with Lord Pitt and Dr Eddie Simon), which has helped to raise awareness and campaign for greater understanding of health issues within the black community.

Dr Franklyn Jacobs, 2005

Dr Anthony Lewis

Dr Anthony Lewis was born in Jamaica. He won a government scholarship to Jamaica College, which he attended from 1954–61. From there he won a scholarship to study dentistry at the University of Leeds. He arrived in the UK in 1962, aged 19. He came over by plane. While studying at Leeds, where he had been the only Caribbean student, he worked as a dentist within the NHS, working in rural Yorkshire and the coalfields. He graduated in 1968 and got a job as a house officer at the Leeds Dental Hospital, where he worked until 1971. He returned to Jamaica, where he became the first dentist appointed to the Bustamante Hospital for Children. In 1999 he was appointed director of dental surgery in the Ministry of Health in Jamaica. He retired from the ministry in 2003 and now runs his own private practice in Barbados.

Dr Anthony Lewis, 2005

Dr Stanley Moonsawmy

Dr Stanley Moonsawmy was born in Guyana. He attended primary and secondary school. In 1956, aged 19, he travelled to Scotland on board a French passenger liner, to study medicine at Edinburgh University. He trained at various hospitals in Edinburgh, graduating in 1965. He started work as a locum, progressing to the position of registrar. He worked at the Royal Infirmary, Edinburgh, until 1973, when he went into general practice, taking over a single-handed practice from a Scottish doctor.

Dr Moonsawmy outside his surgery in Loanhead, 2005

Dr Jean Parboosingh

Dr Jean Parboosingh was born in Jamaica. She attended high school until the age of 18. In 1959, aged 18, she travelled to the UK by ship. She went to Edinburgh where she studied medicine, graduating in 1965. Initially she worked as a houseman, before moving into general practice. In 1978 she and her husband, John Parboosingh, moved to Calgary, Canada. She obtained a masters in community health sciences and worked as a researcher and medical administrator. In 1993 the family moved to Ottawa. She continues to work with the Association of Faculties of Medicine of Canada.

Dr Jean Parboosingh, 2005

Prof John Parboosingh

Professor John Parboosingh was born in Jamaica, where he attended school and college. In 1957, aged 17, he was awarded a place at the faculty of medicine, Edinburgh University. He travelled to Scotland by plane. He graduated in 1964. He did house jobs in Edinburgh, before becoming a senior registrar. In 1972 he was appointed senior lecturer at the Royal Infirmary, Edinburgh. He focused on obstetrics and initiated pioneering work in obstetrics and gynaecology at the Royal Infirmary. In 1978 he took up a post at the University of Calgary, Canada, and moved to Ottawa in 1993 to set up a new e-training programme. He retired in 2001 to concentrate on research.

Professor John Parboosingh, 2005

Chapter 2
Leaving the Caribbean

The women and men who left the Caribbean to work in the NHS did so for various reasons, and the people who were interviewed for this book were no exception. Many were fulfilling childhood dreams to be nurses or doctors. In some cases, family members had worked in the community as nurses, health visitors or midwives. They often exerted a strong influence. Career and training opportunities were also better in Britain than in the Caribbean at that time. Some interviewees had friends and relatives who were already in the UK and so came over to join them. People in this book came to Britain through official recruitment schemes or made their own arrangements. Most had to pay their own expenses.

Three Jamaican immigrants,(left to right) John Hazel, a 21-year-old boxer, Harold Wilmot, 32, and John Richards, a 22-year-old carpenter, arriving at Tilbury on board the ex-troopship SS Empire Windrush, smartly dressed in zoot suits and trilby hats

A passion for nursing

Dr Neslyn Watson-Drueé "had a passion for nursing" and still does. She remembers that as a school prefect, when the midwife and health visitors came to the school, she wanted to learn what they did. She showed early initiative, thinking back to "a young child who had a sore on her leg and nobody wanted to touch it ... I don't think she was being properly looked after at home. I decided to get Dettol at school and clean it and that wound had maggots in it and I remember the look on her face. It brings tears to my eyes as I think about that child. I thought 'Yes, if I could deal with that at that age'. "

Others too had childhood ambitions to nurse, often influenced by older relatives. Sherlene Rudder "… always, always wanted to be a nurse. I had a great admiration for my great-grandmother, who was the district midwife. I don't think she had any formal qualifications but I just remember her going around looking after all these people and I thought this is something I really want to do. I think because she was held in such great esteem I thought 'oh yes I could do with some of that'. Always hearing about nursing, the NHS, that's what I wanted to do, that's really the best place to be trained."

From the age of about two, Joyce Bleasdille-Lumsden had wanted to be a nurse. "I used to make my mud dolls and put an apron and cap on their heads." She helped to deliver her first baby

Joyce Bleasdille-Lumsden accepting an award

"...ALWAYS, ALWAYS WANTED TO BE A NURSE. I HAD A GREAT ADMIRATION FOR MY GREAT-GRANDMOTHER, WHO WAS THE DISTRICT MIDWIFE. I DON'T THINK SHE HAD ANY FORMAL QUALIFICATIONS BUT I JUST REMEMBER HER GOING AROUND LOOKING AFTER ALL THESE PEOPLE AND I THOUGHT THIS IS SOMETHING I REALLY WANT TO DO." Sherlene Rudder

when she was 10. Her great-aunt was a major influence. She "was the old lady in the village. She wasn't a qualified midwife but if anything happened like births, or if someone was sick, they always used to get her." Joyce was her favourite niece, and often accompanied her great-aunt, helping her with leeches and cupping. "It was my job to wash the leeches out and wash the blood from the cups. So she says to me, 'you want to be a nurse, Mrs Norbert is having her child, let's go down and you will see how to deliver her baby.' So I went down there and they went to call the midwife. It was raining, her husband went with a donkey and while he was away, the midwife wasn't there yet and the baby was delivered. My great-aunt boiled the scissors on the fire in the middle of the straw house and she cut the cord and showed me what to do. The lady had no baby clothes so I took a pillowcase and cut the neck and the sleeves and we put it on the baby."

Louise Garvey remembers when she first knew she wanted to be a nurse: "I had an auntie that was ill and she came to see my other auntie. I can remember she had a white dress on and white shoes on and a white cap and I can remember the uniform, it had like turned-up sleeves and she was carrying a black bag. I saw her and I thought that's what I want to be and I've never strayed from that …"

As a child, Lena Hunt "saw a film about nursing in Great Ormond Street in the town, which inspired me, and then I saw an advertisement in a women's magazine when I was about 12 or 13 years old asking for people who were interested in doing nurse training in England. I filled it out and I received a very nice reply back saying, 'You are a little young, but you could try again in a few years' time.' This I did about four years later through the Colonial Office and they sorted out a hospital which accepted me."

For T Anderson, "the professions available with my qualifications were teaching, telegraphy and nursing. I don't think I wanted to be a teacher and if I did, I couldn't because to be a good grade teacher you had to pass music and I'm tone deaf! I can't tell a quaver from a semi-quaver! So I opted for nursing. My main influence – beside my mother wanting the best profession for her children – was my cousin who was the health visitor at one of the district's health centres."

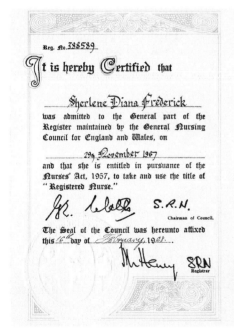

Left: Sherlene Rudder's general nursing certificate, November 1967
Right: T Anderson (sitting down) at graduation, City Hospital

Recruitment

After World War Two, there was a strong recruitment drive in the Caribbean for workers to come to Britain, not just to help the newly formed NHS but also to provide much needed labour in other fields. Contributors to this book responded.

Denzil Nurse came to the UK through British recruitment for workers. Nursing was not his first choice. He "wanted to go into the air force. In those days you had people from Britain coming to recruit from the different services, for example the army, the air force and transportation, and other services. I had a choice of nursing and air force but my first choice was the air force. When I went for the interview I was deemed immature! In fact the sergeant recruiting officer said, 'does your mother know that you're leaving home?' I said, 'Of course, she brought me here!' Due to that, I took my second choice, which was nursing. At that time we had choices of different hospitals and places. I threw the arrow and it landed on Stanley Royd Hospital in Wakefield, Yorkshire."

Dr Neslyn Watson-Druée says her "interest in coming to England really was as a direct recruitment through Enoch Powell, the then Minister of Health who came into the Caribbean and, as they are doing now, was recruiting from the Caribbean … "

Dr Nola Ishmael started her working life as an infant school teacher in Barbados but changed to nursing. "I've always been interested in what nurses did from the books I've read. So when recruitment in the West Indies was at its peak, in the late 1950s, early 1960s, some of my school friends had come to England to be nurses. They

Dr Nola Ishmael at preliminary training school, Whittington hospital, 1969

had written to me to tell me how wonderful it was and so I went to the recruitment office and sought to go to England to do nursing."

Dr Victor Eastmond's main interest was always dentistry, but he did not have the qualifications to enter university. He "attained a job in the government service in Barbados … I worked in the sector where we were sending immigrants to London. I realised a lot of people were getting this opportunity and I decided to enter that programme myself and I applied to work on London Transport. I left Barbados in 1964 at the age of 19 to emigrate to England, which was considered the mother country."

After leaving school, Caswell Jeffrey trained as a carpenter in Jamaica. "They were advertising for people to come to this country from the West Indies. I had a friend and he came over and he encouraged me to come. I came over in 1960 by ship."

Some recruitment programmes were intended to equip Caribbeans with the necessary qualifications to return and use their expertise in their homeland. Dr Anthony Lewis left Jamaica in 1962 to study dentistry at the University of Leeds. At the time "there was a big need for dentists in Jamaica and the government was offering these scholarships and I was successful. I came to the UK in 1962. I remember it was a very, very bad winter that year. I came over by British Airways and landed at Heathrow Airport."

Career and training

Joyce sitting on the steps of Richmond Hill Sanatorium in Grenada, 1958

Some of the contributors to this book had already qualified or trained and worked in the Caribbean. Britain offered the opportunity for further specialist training and for advancing their careers. The NHS was highly regarded and medical training in Britain was considered to be the best.

Joyce Bleasdille-Lumsden had gained experience in nursing before coming to the UK. She did voluntary work at the then Colony Hospital and the St David pharmacy in Grenada. "I started in the Colony Hospital as a probationer when I was 18 and then transferred to the Richmond Hill Sanatorium … I was encouraged by the matron who was from St Vincent to go to England to do my general training, which she thought I was capable of doing rather than working as a nursing assistant. She bought a *Nursing Mirror* and we applied to many hospitals and the Stoke Mandeville Group … accepted me for student nurse training".

Dr Franklyn Jacobs did his medical training at the University of the West Indies, which he describes as "one of the best decisions of my life" because the calibre of the teaching was high. He worked in Trinidad for some years, married and had children. In 1972 he "returned with my family to St Vincent where it quickly became apparent that there was a great need for anaesthetists on the island." He found himself "in the deep end, resorting to self-tuition in anaesthetics." This

Left: Daisy V V Anson **Right:** *Lynette Richards-Murray in Guyana working as a civil servant*

triggered his decision "to train further and so I found myself venturing across the sea to this island of Britain."

Daisy V V Anson wanted "to go to another country and see how other people live and to work and get money. I came over in September 1956 by ship. I enjoyed the ship ride."

Derek Harty "really wanted to go into medicine but at that stage I didn't have the qualifications to do that. I tried getting into the hospital and do laboratory work at the Kingston Public Hospital doing the same laboratory work that I'm doing here [in the UK]. I settled for a job in the research department and spent about four years in that job

after I left school. My mother first of all came to the UK six or seven years before I did, she was employed here. She managed to borrow some money to book my passage to come to this country."

Thelma Lewis "was a nurse in Guyana at St Joseph's Mercy Hospital, a Roman Catholic hospital, so I was already qualified. I did my training for three years and then I did staffing for one year. I came to do further nursing and I'm still here! I came over on the 10 December 1955 by boat, the *SS Colombie* and I was 22 years of age. I had one friend who was here, we were batch mates from nursing, she came up a year ahead of me and

I thought I would follow her."

A teacher at Siburnie Ramharry's school inspired her to take up a career as a dietician. "We had a teacher who had just come back from England who was a domestic science teacher and when I was wondering what I really ought do she said there was a career in dietetics and maybe I would like to apply for that. She got me a lot of information. I wrote around to a lot of different colleges and universities and the one that I was interested in was in Scotland because they offered two courses a year, one in September and one in January and because my A level results came out quite late to get into the September course anywhere I decided to take the January one rather than waste time."

Leila Ghartey initially worked in the Guyana civil service in the central medical laboratory attached to the main hospital in Georgetown. "It was technical work primarily in bacteriology. I enjoyed it very much.

"I became very interested in bacteriology and I thought it might be very interesting to pursue studies in it. I had already done four years in the civil service and at that time the annual leave entitlement was very generous in that you worked for four years and you were allowed six months' leave. So I then took the opportunity to come to Britain and I resigned my post at the hospital and came here to hopefully start studying."

Many rivers to cross

Making my own arrangements

CABLES: WITRACOM, LONDON

TELEPHONE: GROSVENOR 3871/5
,,   7681/2

THE COMMISSION IN THE UNITED KINGDOM FOR THE WEST INDIES,

BRITISH GUIANA AND BRITISH HONDURAS

YOUR REF.:

OUR REF.: P.44/15

REPLIES SHOULD BE ADDRESSED TO:
SECRETARY FOR STUDENT AFFAIRS.

6-10, BRUTON STREET,
LONDON, W.1.

12th May, 1960.

Dear Miss Bleasdille,

As you will know, correspondence has taken place between this office and the Secretary of the Nursing Selection Committee in Grenada concerning your application for Pupil Assistant nursing training in this country.

2.   Subsequent to informing you that the Matron of Harefield Hospital was unable to accept you, we were advised that you were prepared to accept the vacancy offered by Tindal General Hospital.

3.   Arrangements were made to meet you on arrival through the British Council. We understand that you proceeded to your present address. We have been informed that you have applied to the Yardley Green Hospital in Birmingham.

4.   Please inform this office of your reasons for now acting on your own behalf, and until your reply is received, this office is unable to support any applications you may make for nursing training to any other hospital.

Yours sincerely,

(Miss) Sheila McEachrane
for Secretary, Student Affairs Division

Miss Joyce Bleasdille,
20, Turners Place,
Weedon,
Nr. Aylesbury,
Bucks.

Letter received by Joyce Bleasdille-Lumsden from the Commission in the United Kingdom for the West Indies, British Guiana and British Honduras

Many of those who wanted to work in the NHS applied directly to hospitals in the UK. Some responded to advertisements. Sherlene Rudder was one. She made her "own arrangements really because lots of my colleagues were going off to the States and London Transport. I wrote off to a hospital in Kent called Pembury. Somebody gave me a *Nursing Times,* I think, and I saw it there and wrote off and they said if I came I would be interviewed. I came over to the UK and lived with my parents who lived in Paddington, wrote off, did the exam and I was accepted."

Elizabeth Yates did similarly but she had to take her exams in Guyana before being accepted. She worked as a geography teacher in Guyana for two terms in a secondary school but decided teaching "wasn't for me! That was when I started exploring again what I was going to do. My uncle, who was a doctor, studied here [in the UK] and had brought back information about occupational therapy … That's how I heard about occupational therapy. I wrote to the School of Occupational Therapists and they sent me a list of schools and then I wrote to a number. The London school which I eventually attended sent details asking if an invigilator could be found so I could sit the exam, which was a mixture of psychological testing and an essay … I did that and was successful and left to come to England to study."

Family connections

Dr Neslyn Watson-Druée could have gone to Canada to nurse but chose England "because my father served in World War Two here and I wanted to see what the country was like … also my paternal grandmother is first generation Scots and Irish and I wanted that connection." Her parents were not keen. "My father felt that nursing was a very underpaid profession and he felt that I should stay and complete my A levels and enter the teaching profession. I disagreed with him … and in some ways I wasn't absolutely 100 per cent straight … I said I was going on holiday and at that time he had to sign my passport because you had to be 21 before you could sign for your passport in those days. For me it was quite a bit of, I suppose, exploration really and when I think back now I don't know how I had the courage to do that, but I did."

Both of Professor John Parboosingh's parents were physicians and his sister was also going into medicine. As he says: "I didn't have much choice really. At the age of 17 after high school examinations I applied to the University of Edinburgh and was successful as a candidate for the faculty of medicine. I came over to the UK in 1957 by plane. I was on my own, but I was coming to two sisters who were already in London. I was excited."

Dr Jean Parboosingh had wanted to pursue a medical career from an early age. "I came to

Britain in 1959. My grandparents were still alive in Edinburgh at the time and my older brother had already gone to Edinburgh to study a year ahead of me and so I had family there. I was 18 when I left Jamaica and I travelled by ship and was met by my brother and an aunt who were also in the London area at the time."

Dr Stanley Moonsawmy's father influenced his

decision to study medicine. "I was thinking of a medical career … I came to study medicine at Edinburgh University as arranged and for which I had applied a few months before as most of my father's friends were Edinburgh graduates in medicine and therefore I was more or less influenced by him to come here to study medicine."

Joining relatives

Most people interviewed who left the Caribbean already had relatives in the UK, who had come over earlier to work. When Nelson Auguste "first came to this country my brother came over before me and then sent for me and I started to work and make a living."

Inez Stewart left Jamaica to join her father and brother who were already in England. "I came to the UK when I was 21 years old on the 22 September 1960, by plane. My Dad was living here and he sent for me and my brother. I was a bit nervous, as I had never flown before. My dad was at the airport to meet me and we went straight to Sheffield."

Olivine Benjamin "came to the UK because my father had just died and the rest of my family thought it best that I joined my brother here which would make it easier on the rest of the family back home. I didn't know what to expect and I was excited. I came over in 1965 with my niece, my brother's daughter, and we came by plane. We arrived in Manchester airport and then we caught the coach to Sheffield."

"I CAME TO THE UK WHEN I WAS 21 YEARS OLD ON THE 22 SEPTEMBER 1960, BY PLANE. MY DAD WAS LIVING HERE AND HE SENT FOR ME AND MY BROTHER. I WAS A BIT NERVOUS, AS I HAD NEVER FLOWN BEFORE. MY DAD WAS AT THE AIRPORT TO MEET ME AND WE WENT STRAIGHT TO SHEFFIELD."
Inez Stewart

Left: Olivine Benjamin (third from left) celebrating Christmas with colleagues in the 1980s *Right:* Inez Stuart (right) on a day out with a patient

Making the journey

Caribbeans travelled to the UK by ship or plane, usually by ship. The journey by ship took two to three weeks. For many it was a journey into the unknown. Some travelled alone, others with friends and relatives. From 1955 the British and Barbados governments provided loans and there was some sponsorship, but most people paid their own passage, or had to replay loans at a later stage. Parents too often funded the fares.

Dr Stanley Moonsawmy remember that "in those days, in 1956, most of the transport from the Caribbean was by ship not plane and so it was a French passenger liner which collected me and my mother to bring us across the Atlantic to Plymouth, and then a train up to London."

Erena Kydd left St Vincent in 1959 "because of adventure. Everybody was leaving at that time, so I wanted a bit of what was going on!" She came over by boat. "There were lots of people from different areas in the country. We came from a small boat from St Vincent to Trinidad, spent a week in Trinidad and then left Trinidad and boarded the *Erskine* to come to England."

Dr Nola Ishmael "came by plane to London Airport, now Heathrow. I travelled with a number of people who went to different hospitals. I remember being at the airport in Bridgetown; it was called Seawell at the time. When it was my turn to go through the departure gates, there was a person who was checking the names off. I said my name but they didn't have me on the list and I thought gosh if I get sent back my dad would say 'If you were meant to go, you would of gone, so you're not going.' So while he was busy checking other people I walked on the plane and sat down! … My ticket was financed by loans from the Barbados government, which we all had to pay back."

Louise Garvey "came to England in 1957 when I was 15 and a half, by plane. Most of my friends were migrating to England and my grandfather said to my grandma one day, 'I think it's time that you sent Louise to her mother.' So my grandmother sort of got everything that was needed; the necessary papers. Before I came across, my grandma had heard that England was so cold;

The British liner SS Empire Windrush *at port, 28 March 1954*

Joyce Bleasdille-Lumsden (left) on a boat to England, March 1960

when I was growing up they used to say I'm very delicate. So what she did she got the Jamaican newspaper, because she heard that it would keep you warm, and she cut that out and made it into a vest. So that went onto my slip that I had on and then she made a red vest and put it over that and that kept me really warm coming across from Jamaica to England!"

For Lena Hunt, "it was a great adventure for me to travel all that way on my own. I had quite a long rough journey and it all seemed very busy and bewildering."

Lucy Martin-Burnham left Jamaica in 1951. "Following a discussion with my mother, I decided to go to England to do my nurse training, and she financed the fare. I was given the address of a friend who was working at Amersham General Hospital in Buckinghamshire. I wrote to this address and matron wrote to me to go to an interview at the Ministry of Health in Jamaica. I wrote back to say I am on my way to visit a friend in England and will come and see her in person and I got an interview … I boarded the ship at Port Antonio and … travelled on *Elders and Fyfe*. It was a small boat with 12 passengers. I was on the boat for 14 days. I was the only black person and found it a little strange. It was a mixture of excitement in that I was going in uncharted waters but there was a job at the end."

Trinidadian Gloria Falode left the Caribbean in 1960, when she was 23. A friend had given her the address of a cousin in England. She had already written to Hammersmith Hospital, who asked her to come up for an interview. Her mother "said no, what would happen if you want over there and failed then where would you stay … you had to listen to reason. Saxondale Hospital … wrote back to me and I showed it to my mother and she thought it was a good idea. After sending the forms and a picture they accepted me, they told me what my salary would be and that I would be living in the nurses' home, so once my mother saw that and then I told her about my friend Shirley,

who had a cousin there … My big brother Patrick booked my passage to come over … They said you must have flannelette pyjamas, so my aunt made me some … I suppose when you're young you don't think about such a great distance … The journey lasted 14 days."

Lynette Richards-Murray sailed from Guyana to the UK. She had been working as a civil servant and saw advertisements for nurse training. "Because I wanted to do nurse training I applied to hospitals. Then I was advised that the warmest part of England was Somerset! So that's why I

"BECAUSE I WANTED TO DO NURSE TRAINING I APPLIED TO HOSPITALS. THEN I WAS ADVISED THAT THE WARMEST PART OF ENGLAND WAS SOMERSET! SO THAT'S WHY I APPLIED TO TAUNTON IN SOMERSET AND THEY ACCEPTED ME. I CAME OVER IN FEBRUARY 1959 AND I WAS 20. I CAME OVER BY SHIP. IT WAS THE *ORANJESTAD*. IT TOOK THREE WEEKS TO GET HERE ... MY FATHER DECIDED I SHOULD GO WITH MY ELDER SISTER. SO I ACTUALLY SAVED UP FOR MY SISTER SO SHE COULD COME OVER WITH ME."
Lynette Richards-Murray

Joyce Bleasdille-Lumsden (third from right) on a boat to England, March 1960

56

Left: Margaret Knight, King's College Hospital during nurse training, 1949 **Right:** *Sherlene Rudder*

applied to Taunton in Somerset and they accepted me. I came over in February 1959 and I was 20. I came over by ship. It was the *Oranjestad*. It took three weeks to get here … My father decided I should go with my elder sister. So I actually saved up for my sister so she could come over with me."

Sherlene Rudder considers she was one of the "fortunate ones to fly. I came by BOAC. With no company, I was absolutely terrified and very inappropriately clad … because even though my mum had said it's cold here … you don't imagine anything being that cold!"

Margaret Knight "travelled to England on a French ship. It was called the *Gascoigne*. It travelled from Barbados, stopping at Martinique and Guadeloupe. In Martinique we were allowed to disembark and we walked around Fort-de-France and had lunch in a restaurant. It was the first time I had eaten mountain chicken [a special kind of frog and a French delicacy]. I almost vomited when I was told what I had eaten."

M Bussue travelled from St Kitts in 1958 with two children, to join her husband who had come to England to find work. She "travelled with my brother-in-law plus a friend of mine … It was a proper liner. It was very comfortable, nice and clean … it had every comfort. As I had the two children the sailors were very good with their meals, they would give them special stuff being two and three years old. It took 13 days. We had four stops. We went to Barbados, Martinique and

Azores and never went ashore but when we came to Spain we went ashore for a few hours. We were so shocked at the poverty there compared to what we had on the ship."

Hazel Watson came to England on a government recruitment scheme. "I was about 14 years old when I left school. My mum sent me to do domestic science and that went on in the pavilion; lots of craftwork. I went to learn to sew and do needlework before I came to the UK. I wrote to various hospitals in England asking for job opportunities. Quite a few replied with 'no' but one said 'yes' so I took that one. My passage was paid for by the government scheme. I left home 9 May 1957 and I was nearly 17 years old. I came by ship with a friend, we met when I went for my interview

to get my passage, my mum was talking to this young woman and discovered she was going to the same hospital, so she was pleased for me because she was older and I wasn't just coming on my own. We became good friends, she was also a nurse but she sadly passed away. We also met another lady, she had a couple of toddlers and we became fairly good mates and we sort of looked after each other. We had a few stopovers; Tenerife, Barcelona and Paris and then we came to Victoria Station."

Dr Eddie Adams's sister paid for him to take his A levels in Guyana. Following school, he was awarded a grant to study medicine at King's College, London. He travelled on the *SS Colombie*, the same ship that brought Thelma Lewis to the UK two years later.

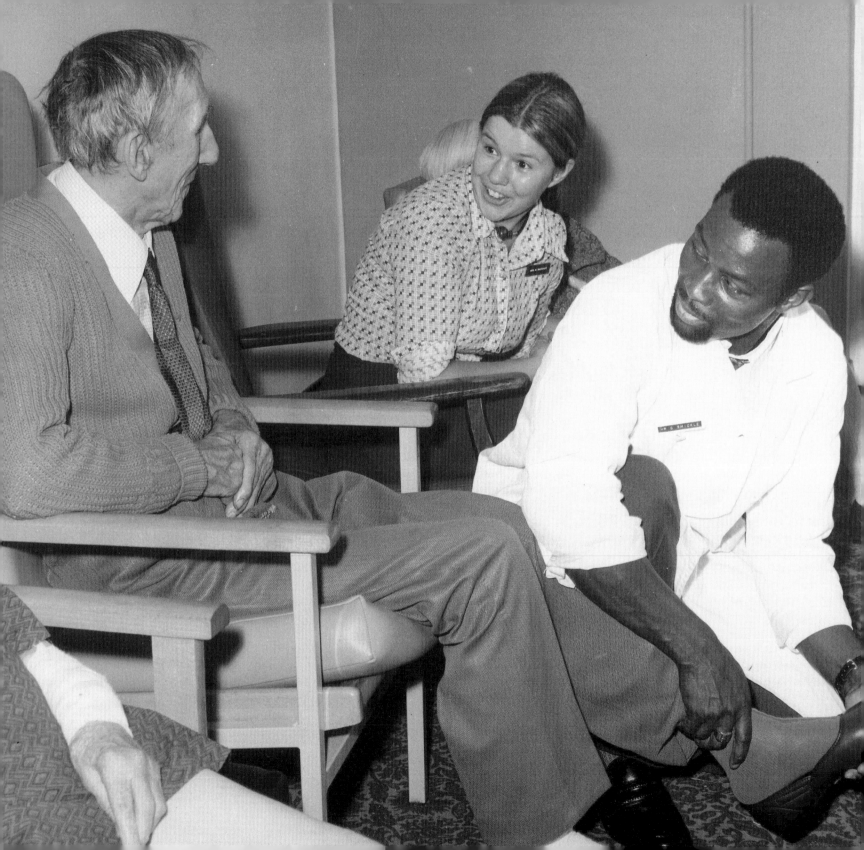

Chapter 3

First Impressions

People interviewed for this book had a lot to say about their first impressions of Britain. No matter what they had learned before coming, all of them noticed great differences between the Caribbean and the UK, particularly in terms of language, housing, customs and, of course, food and climate. After the Caribbean, Britain looked grey and drab. There were many surprises. Some found the new experience exciting; others felt rather lonely and homesick. But everyone stayed.

Auxiliary nurse assisting a patient at St Clements Hospital,
Bow, c1970s (Royal London Hospital Archives: SC/P/8)

A welcome

Representatives from the British Council, the Colonial Office or the Salvation Army welcomed many of the new arrivals. Dr Stanley Moonsawmy found them "very, very kind and very good."

The British Council met Denzil Nurse. "That was my first encounter with the British culture. I remember going into the house and I was offered a cup of tea and I threw the water on the fire because I thought the house was on fire! She said, 'Did you not know that's for heating?' She made me comfortable and put me on the train from Liverpool (Lime Street) to Wakefield (West Gate).

That was another experience because I had never travelled on a train before. I saw nothing … it was fog all the way! My cousin had already warned me about the fog and he used to tell me if you put your hand out you couldn't see your fingers! I didn't believe him until I saw it."

Muriel Bussue had not been on a train either. She was met by the Salvation Army and thought "they were brilliant because we travelled from Southampton to Victoria Station by train and as I had these two children they came up to me and said 'Do the children need a drink of water or the toilet or anything?' which was very good."

When Lena Hunt arrived at Southampton, "it all seemed very busy and bewildering but I was met by someone from the Colonial Office … who put me on a train to Redhill Hospital. I was handed over to the people who look after new recruits. There were students from all parts of the world. We were a fair-sized family on the island and as I've grown older, I think I miss my home more than I did."

The British Council for Overseas Students came to meet Joyce Bleasdille-Lumsden. They "put a tag on me with my name and address and I went into a minibus and they showed us around London. Everything was strange to me. The people all wore black clothes and the traffic lights. I had never seen a traffic light before! They showed us Buckingham Palace but I wasn't interested! I was more interested in how the people were walking, busy, busy, busy!"

Nola Ishmael arrived at London Airport where the British Council met her and took her to Victoria Station where her sister met her with "a wonderful coat". From there she went to Bishops Stortford Hospital, where the home sister met her. "We had had a long journey and were really exhausted. Home sister suggested we come into the dining room for a cup of tea and I can tell you I have never tasted a better cup of tea since! That was the best cup of tea in my whole life! I can tell you it refreshed parts that haven't been refreshed since then!"

Family support

Relatives met many of the new arrivals. They came armed with warm clothes and provided a welcome support in the strange new country.

Siburnie Ramharry's brother was already studying in London and met her when she arrived in England. "Arriving … in the middle of winter was not very nice … I think for somebody coming from the Caribbean for the first time without one's family, it's quite a strange experience. Luckily my brother was just a phone call away."

Olivine Benjamin arrived in Manchester and then took the coach to Sheffield, where her brother met her. "He brought this big coat and I thought Oh! We weren't used to coats or things like that, but it was March and it was very cold. My brother had his own home with seven of his children and we all lived quite happily. Sometimes I did get homesick … the worst bit was leaving my mum back home and my other brothers and sisters."

Sherlene Rudder was "absolutely terrified" when she arrived and "very inappropriately clad as well … you don't imagine anything being that cold … Luckily my mother was at the airport waiting for me with some decent clothing! … I remember as we were landing I was looking out and I saw it was grey and dreadful. I thought it looked absolutely terrible and it was dark. I found my mum there who I hadn't seen since I was 12 so that was fabulous, it really was."

Louise Garvey's mother too was waiting for her.

Lena Hunt (first nurse on the left) on the ward at Christmas time

"I felt very lonely because of course I was leaving all my cousins and everyone back home. When I came off the plane … [it] gave me the impression of living in an icebox! My mum came to meet me … I was so glad to see her. I just sort of fell in her arms and she brought along this like Red Riding Hood coat. It was a long coat with fur around the tail, around the sleeves and it had a hood on it and had fur around that."

First impressions

Tryphena Anderson's "first impressions of England were, 'Oh god how dreary!' The chimneys I didn't believe they were houses. 'What were they? Were these factories?' I realised straight away that reading English literature I didn't understand a thing. I would have to read it again and consider, because these were the chimney tops that you read about in Grimm's fairy tales; people going down the chimneys and Dickens's books. I thought, I'm going to really appreciate it now; it's not just words.

"White people were not dressing like you're used to seeing them dress in Jamaica. So it was like a camera going, click, click, click!."

But Tryphena Anderson's biggest shock was "seeing ordinary white people doing ordinary work. You were sort of made to believe that they lived in a more aristocratic way, that they didn't clean floors and they didn't sweep streets. I couldn't understand any of what they were saying! Frankly, I think I spoke better English than most of them!"

For Elizabeth Yates, "the terraced houses … were strange because, back home, so to speak, we don't have joined-up houses. I thought it was really weird that people wanted to live all joined up next to each other. The second thing was the food: kind of no taste, lack of spices. The third thing that struck me was when you're in the West Indies in the 1960s and you saw English people they were in positions of power and it was really strange to see white people sweeping streets and doing manual jobs. I had not seen that before."

Lucy Martin-Burnham found it all "quite strange really because I suppose I was comparing England with Jamaica: the brightly coloured buildings, nice and clean looking, then of course I came into this docklands and it was very drab and I suppose in a way I was disappointed. It was quite different to what I expected."

Gloria Falode found the British accents strange: "In the West Indies all you hear about is BBC English, I was never exposed to any other dialect. They would say, 'Yes me duck' and those sorts of things and I couldn't understand what they were saying!"

Derek Harty's first impression of Britain was that "it was a very strange place. I just didn't like it at first. I really went through a terrible period where I wanted to go back. For the first two or three weeks I was very upset. I really wanted to go back to my country."

Leila Ghartey found public transport confusing. "The fact that you had to plan your route before leaving home was quite something and several times I got lost, I wasn't used to using public transport and that was something I had to learn and understand how to do." She also "had my first attack of chilblains that made my life absolutely intolerable!"

Tryphena Anderson (second from right) with colleagues at Coppice Hospital, 1961

Culture shocks

For Dr Stanley Moonsawmy "it was a bit of a cultural shock in that transport and housing was so totally different from the tropical area from which I originated … I thought the people looked very dark and grey in their winter and summer coats. Their faces were so white and pasty! I was then able to put that together with my previous experience in Guyana, whereby our indigenous people, the Red Indian Carib tribes, had a word for the white man, which was the same word for ghost, and I then realised in my own feelings that it was probably a good description!" Looking back to his first years in Edinburgh he thought "the local people were very reserved … they would not speak to you openly; you had to be introduced. I think there was a lot of shyness on both sides in those early days and there was nothing really meant behind it but it was just their culture that I had to adapt to … I noticed they spoke with a stiff upper lip and didn't use their eye contact and their hands or their facial features when they were speaking so they were very formal."

Lynette Richards-Murray found it "surprising when we got here because we had white porters to pick up our luggage and that was one of the first shocks because in Guyana all the white people that we came into contact spoke like Prince Charles and they were in very high positions."

Thelma Lewis arrived in December. "It was very cold, no one spoke to anybody and what surprised me was I stayed one night at the YWCA in Baker Street, looking through the window I saw these buses coming up to one stop. I didn't realise they were different numbers and I wondered why the passengers were not getting on! People were choosing and not because the bus was full up; it was because they were different numbers, which I didn't realise."

Lynette Richards-Murray (third from left) during presentation

Misconceptions

Many interviewees found that what they had learned about Britain in the Caribbean was not the case. Erena Kydd was "amazed because the things that you hear in the Caribbean. It was completely different until you came and saw what it was like. It was very cold and the surroundings were strange. The different speeches: although we speak English, it is broken and the way they would ask you different questions. Sometimes you found it a bit difficult to answer the questions."

Murriel Bussue was surprised to see people wearing "twin sets. All the pictures that we saw of England were with people wearing coats and I remember the first day I went out shopping in C&A and I remember thinking they had dresses without sleeves! I saw clothes that I was accustomed to. I suppose it was like what they had thought about us because they believed we came from monkeys and if they asked us the time our tails would drop."

Dr Franklyn Jacobs went straight from the airport to a lecture at the Royal College of Surgeons. His first impressions were, "I want to get out of here! During the luncheon period, feeling thirsty, I stepped into a pub asking for a glass of iced water. I was met with dumbfounded looks, as if I'd spoken in a foreign language. Apparently they'd never received such a request before, as no one understood what I'd meant!"

Margaret Knight arrived in 1949 and was very aware of how much Britain had suffered from the war, particularly bomb damage. She loved the countryside but was surprised to see large advertisements that "proclaimed: 'This is the Strong country'. I wondered what was 'strong' about the countryside. It never dawned on me that by 'Strong' they were referring to Hampshire ale! It was a great pleasure to see the green fields and pastures, with cows and sheep grazing, and to pass through little villages along the way. This was the part of England that I liked."

Caswell Jeffrey thought the UK "was quite strange! I missed my family but I knew I came here with the intentions of making things better. I made myself quite comfortable and at home."

Caswell Jeffrey (left) at work with colleagues

"I WANT TO GET OUT OF HERE! DURING THE LUNCHEON PERIOD, FEELING THIRSTY, I STEPPED INTO A PUB ASKING FOR A GLASS OF ICED WATER. I WAS MET WITH DUMBFOUNDED LOOKS, AS IF I'D SPOKEN IN A FOREIGN LANGUAGE. APPARENTLY THEY'D NEVER RECEIVED SUCH A REQUEST BEFORE, AS NO ONE UNDERSTOOD WHAT I'D MEANT!"
Dr Franklyn Jacobs

Food

Everyone interviewed for this book commented on the British food – it was one of the biggest culture shocks of all. Joyce Bleasdille-Lumsden went straight to the hospital where she was to work. It was midnight and "the night sister was waiting for me because she knew I was coming. When I reached the hospital the night sister said, 'Are you hungry?' and I said, 'Yes'. They brought me scrambled egg and toast and I shall never forget that scrambled egg! It had so much water in it. It didn't look like our West Indian scrambled egg but I was hungry so I had to eat it and it had no salt!"

Dr Victor Eastmond confessed that when he left Barbados he did not know how to cook so coming to England, he had to eat what he was given. "That was a bit of shock. The type of food we would have in the Caribbean is a lot more spicy and tasty. The food over in the UK was bland with less salt. I was used to more of a rice diet and over here was more of a potato diet."

Neslyn Watson-Drueé "was amazed at the difference in the light; that hit me most. In the Caribbean at four o'clock in the morning, it is bright! Also, the food was bland, it was as far as I'm concerned tasteless and I had difficulty in digesting it. Food was problematic for the want of a better word."

For Hazel Watson, "it's the tea I wasn't very keen on." For Tryphena Anderson, "the beef was raw and it was stringy! I couldn't get used to

beans. There was no spice; everything was cooked different. One night I remember I was working on the ENT ward and I checked when I went for my tea that the supper was going to be Welsh rarebit and I thought oh good! I hadn't eaten rabbit and I was so excited. I made sure I did everything so when they did their checklist I could get to that dining room. When I got to that dining room guess what it was? Cheese on toast! I didn't like their cheese anyway!"

Lynette Richards-Murray remembered that people were "very kind and generous" but "the food was something else. I just couldn't come to terms with the food because I remember the first time I had steak and kidney pie. I can still smell the wee in the pie! On Fridays we used to have fish

and chips. It looked lovely, brown and nice but there was no seasoning! I used to live on cheese and biscuits! Of course I put on a lot of weight!"

In her interview, Gloria Falode remembered: "We didn't like the food; the curries had sultanas in them. At Christmas time we used to get parcels from home and everybody's parents used to send them pepper sauce, it was like gold dust! One day matron decided she wanted to see all of us and we thought we had done something bad and she was asking why we were not going to the dining room. They were concerned we were not eating properly so we told her and she said, could we go and see the chef and tell him what we wanted. The whole dietary thing changed because of us."

Homesickness and excitement

Many interviewees talked about being homesick and missing their families and friends when they first arrived. But despite the strangeness many of the new arrivals were very excited to be in Britain.

Lynette Richards-Murray remembered: "For the first month I didn't hear from my parents and I was inconsolable. Everyday I looked out for this letter and thinking, 'well, what's going on?' I really thought they'd died! I missed my parents, especially my father because he was my guiding light. He used to advise me to do things. I missed his voice telling me things."

Dr Victor Eastmond "missed playing football. I missed the sport and the camaraderie that I had growing up with those persons whom I had left behind. My group was put up in a very small apartment in Kensington, which was actually owned by a Barbadian. We shared facilities with lots of Barbadians who were also immigrants. I remember when I left the airport my initial impression on that November morning was that England was a very dirty and miserable place. The weather was very overcast, dark and gloomy. The cars were dirty and unwashed and a lot of mess on the roads. I was not happy with what I saw. Then when I got down to where I was going to reside, I left the home to explore the area. While walking the streets I stepped into some dog mess and that again did not give me a very good impression of the mother country. This was something I wasn't used to in my own smaller 'Little England', Barbados."

Nola Ishmael was "keen to see the types of people that were around, the busy-ness of London and the whole ambience engaged me. I was quite interested in what was going on and I did a lot of staring. I daresay I was learning as I stared. Let me tell you this was the swinging sixties and I swung with the Beatles and the Rolling Stones. This was the era of Cilla Black. As the sixties rolled on, we were very much part of the new phenomenon of music and we used to go the cinema. So, homesick, no! I was too busy absorbing and feeling excited."

Sherlene Rudder missed her grandmother but thought that being in England "was really an exciting adventure. I loved that. A friend of the family took me around London and that was very exciting."

It was summer when Professor John Parboosingh arrived, "so the weather was excellent and the different types of people and the population of London were really quite striking to me. I was sort of prepared because my sisters were there before, so they got me a coat and things like that. The biggest shock was independence and having to look after myself. I had a sister already there in medical school so with her help I found digs. I was not particularly homesick, more excited and worried because of getting back into school. There were many West Indians, approximately 10 or 15 in each medical school class, and West Indian associations. I certainly joined that with my sister and lots of social activities."

Jean Parboosingh also found the experience exciting. "We did some sightseeing in the London area and went up to Edinburgh. I had a couple of months before the university actually started so I could get to know the people and the area … I had to learn to cook and do everything for myself. I wasn't homesick. I got letters from home every week. There wasn't easy access to the telephone and email didn't exist in those days but having family helped and, like my husband John, I joined the West Indian association and went to all their parties so it was also fun."

Dr Anthony Lewis found the differences "stimulating. The weather funnily enough didn't bother me at all. I was properly clad and it was just a new venture and exciting for a young man and I really enjoyed it … I went straight to Yorkshire and also got into brand new halls of residence at the University of Leeds called Bodington Hall, with central heating! I was really very privileged … I was not homesick at all. I came from a very close and loving family. My father had been in England on one of these education courses, he was a teacher. So he had spoken to me about what to expect."

Chapter 4
Joining the NHS

Most Caribbean nurses, doctors and health practitioners started work with the NHS as soon as they arrived in Britain. Several people in this book joined the NHS as trainee nurses. Their first few weeks and months were often exhausting. Pay was low, hours were long and the work and training were intensive. Some were disappointed to find they were not doing the work or training they had expected but they persevered. Others arrived in Britain, and then looked for work in the NHS. Many first-generation Caribbean recruits were the first in their hospital. Most received help and support from matrons, sisters and patients.

Nurses greeting Frederick Angel, 14 April 1962

Pupil nurses

Until 1986 there were two levels of nurse training: 'staff' or SRN (State Registered Nursing) and 'pupil' or SEN (State Enrolled Nursing). SRN included ward management; SEN was shorter and more clinically focused. Caribbean nurses had expected to do SRN training.

Neslyn Watson-Druée was disappointed that, "after being met by the home sister, two or three days later, the matron informed me that the group of hospitals had its GNC inspection the week prior to me arriving and that the group was downgraded from SRN training to SEN training." Neslyn was given the choice of leaving or staying. "I did not have anywhere to leave to and I didn't want to work as an auxiliary, so I started the SEN training and the matron promised that under the circumstances, because I came for the SRN training, she would do all that she could to get me a good school ... just before I took the SEN final examination, I applied [to Tunbridge Wells] for SRN training on her recommendation."

Joyce Bleasdille-Lumsden had been accepted for student nurse training at Tynesdale General Hospital. "The next morning when I saw the matron ... she sent me to the sewing room to be measured for uniform. They had me measured for a green uniform and I saw one or two nurses in purple uniform. So when I went back I asked my Jamaican friend what is the green uniform? She said, 'We are pupil nurses, a lower grade of nurses, stupid nurses,' and I went back to the matron and I said to her I was accepted for student nurse training and not pupil nurse training. I had to do the pupil nurse training, otherwise they would send me back to Grenada."

Left: Trphena Anderson (first row, far right, sitting down) with colleagues at Coppice Hospital, 1961 **Right:** Nola Ishmael's health visitors' certificate

Nurse training

Training involved academic study and work on the wards. Trainee nurses, particularly BME nurses, did everything from cleaning wards to washing out sluices. Some Caribbean recruits felt this was not 'proper' nursing.

For Nola Ishmael, "academic learning wasn't a problem, it was the physical exhaustion and requirement to manage the heavy lifting, to keep going no matter what and the early rising to go on duty at 7.30am … We had a night or home sister who would knock on the doors to get us up to start day duty. The first few weeks of the job was a certain amount of bewilderment, naivety and feeling one of a number. However, the hospital was very nurturing, they cared for us nurses from overseas."

After six weeks of learning practical things, such as anatomy, Lena Hunt started working on the wards. "It was very, very hard work and very long hours. Nurses did a lot of the cleaning jobs, such as damp dusting, washing and ironing bandages. There were no disposable bedpans. Male 'bottles' [urinals], syringes, needles, tubing, waterproof mattress covers, dressing and 'procedure' packs, they all had to be cleaned and reused. Bed castors had to be in a straight line down both sides of the ward when the sister checked after the daily cleaning round. Gauze dressings were cut from large rolls, folded and packed in lots of 10, along with hand-rolled cotton wool balls, by the nurses – usually during night duty – into metal drums and sent for sterilisation. It was very hard on our feet. Day shifts started at 7.30am and finished at 8.30pm. Early shift finished at 1pm and late shift was 1pm to 8.30pm."

Erena Kydd's first job in the NHS was as an auxiliary in the Queen Elizabeth Hospital, Birmingham. She was put on the ward but says, "I was more like a domestic. They were saying, 'you go and clean the toilets and the bedpans' … in those days the nurses had to go on their knees and scrub the floors, so one day I went in and I did it for two weeks on a stretch … I wasn't allowed around the patients … I said, 'why me, everyday I come on you're sending me to do the same thing and I haven't seen anybody else do it … I didn't come here to clean bedpans … I left my home and I came to this country and I thought I would better my position, but this, I've never done it at home?"

As a married woman with children, M Bussue thought she would not be able to join the NHS but she applied. "When I got an interview and I took the test they said 'your mark is good enough to do your training', so I said I couldn't because I've got a family. I decided to do six in the evening until 10pm and I never said a word to my husband. So when I got the letter with the starting date he went ballistic and there was an atmosphere for two weeks. The first day … it was strange seeing all these people in bed, when we went to do the bedpan washer I was heaving like I wanted to be sick. This woman she saw me, it was another black woman, she said to me, 'I was just like that before I came', and then she was puffing away on a cigarette and said, 'This is what it made me do!' I said, 'Before I do that I'll leave!' On the second or third day a woman who was living on my road, who worked there, she saw me and said, 'Are you on this afternoon?' and I said, 'I don't know if I'm going, and she said to me to go, and with her encouragement, I went back."

Neslyn Watson-Druée remembers, "horrendous hours during training … my feet were sore and I went and talked to the sister and she said I should rub my feet with methylated spirits to harden my feet up! The work was hard but I came to do nursing and I couldn't go home. My pay was seven pounds two shillings and six pence per week."

For Margaret Knight training included "theory as well as practical. We had to learn how to make beds and how to strip-wash a patient in a bed. There were dummies that we had to practice on and so it was a lot of bed making and first aid – learning how to bandage and that sort of thing. There were no other Caribbean trainees at the time, but there was a very charming girl that I struck up a friendship with; she was from Sierra Leone and her name was Constance. I called her Connie. She and I became very fast friends because we came from a similar background."

Psychiatric nursing

Many Caribbean recruits were placed in psychiatric hospitals, or on geriatric wards. Gloria Falode arrived at her hospital and "saw this imposing looking building.

It was a psychiatric hospital. The night sister came and said, 'Did I want tea?' and she took me to one of the wards and introduced me to the sister and then they put me to sit down by this fire and they

gave me tea. In the morning there was a knock on my door and someone was knocking on all the doors along the corridor saying, '6 o'clock nurse' because they used to wake you up as you were on duty at 7am … we had chains with a key on it, you never had it dangling, it went straight into your pockets and then you put your belt over it. We were told that was for our safety … Your duty was to talk to the patients and listen to them and report anything strange to the sister, as your powers of observation were more acute. We used to do the Gay Gordon dance with patients, where you dance in a ring and had to go up with your hands together and then change partners, it was really elegant."

Thelma Lewis joined the NHS when she started at the Houghton Hospital, Epsom: "The patients seemed normal to me because at home if someone is mad, you back off mate! It wasn't until they flared up and they put them in the padded cell I realised they could get to that degree of aggression. Sadly, I couldn't take that. It was their attitude towards the patient. I thought, 'this is not nursing.' There were other Caribbean students, one girl called Olive from Guyana and two male nurses from Trinidad but I was still very homesick! I was quite prepared to return home within months of arriving, but then we would encourage each other and say, you can't come this distance and let the side down. That sort of thing kept us going."

Gloria Fallode (top row, far right) with fellow nurses, 1960s

Making friends

Caribbean and other overseas recruits supported each other during the first few weeks and months. Some, such as Elizabeth Yates who trained at the London School of Occupational Therapy, arrived to find they were the only Caribbean student.

Nola Ishmael remembers, "We had Trinidadians, people from different countries in Africa, we had people from Mauritius, we had Bajans like myself. We all learnt and supported each other and I made some really good friends at the Whittington."

Lucy Martin-Burnham arrived too early for the hospital training school, so "the matron recommended that I work on the wards, as this would obviously give me good experience. I was very fortunate to have a very understanding sister; she took me under her wing, which was very comforting and reassuring. I started my training in 1951 and was quite excited because it reminded me of my training back in Jamaica, going to school. It was all theory. There were no other Caribbeans training where I was."

Lynette Richards-Murray was the first Guyanese student in her hospital. "Matron knew I was coming and they sent a taxi for me at the train station and I had a very warm welcome there because I was the first Guyanese there. They had a few people from other Caribbean islands. I had a very good Irish friend and in some ways I can see what drew us together because the conditions that were happening in Ireland were the same in Guyana. We had this commonality."

Sherlene Rudder, who joined the NHS at Pembury Hospital, Kent, remembers: "There were lots of students from different Caribbean islands. I made friends with another young lady who had come from Barbados. The sister used to put the fear of God into us and she was very strict but had incredibly high standards … You can appreciate it later but when you first start, it's pretty tough on you."

In Joyce Bleasdille-Lumsden's hospital, "there were only five black nurses from the Caribbean. We had one African nurse, she was a princess from Nigeria, one Trinidadian, one Guyanese, two Barbadians and myself. The next morning the night sister made friends with a Jamaican nurse and she asked her to look after me. Her name was Dorothy Wallace. I couldn't understand her accent, it was different from Grenadian, but we got along fine and she took me to the dining room and to the ward to see matron and then we became very close friends."

Living in the Nurses' Home

Most trainee nurses lived in nurses' homes. Many had to pay their board and lodging; all had to make small salaries stretch a long way.

Louise Garvey recalls that, "I think my first pay was £7 for the month, as I lived in ... Most nurses had to live in then, it was not like now. So it was £7, after they had taken out my board and lodgings and food. You had to be in by 11pm and you had to get a written note from matron if you needed to stay out later than that. Matron would check if you were in and some people climbed out of windows after 11pm!"

Lena Hunt recollects: "Normally we had to live in the nurses' home during training, and be subject to all the rules and regulations of the home sisters. We had to be in by 10.30pm, but if you had a late pass you would have to be in by 11.30pm, after which time the front door to the home was locked and we had to try and get someone to let us in – without letting the sister know if possible – or there would be trouble the next day! The night porters often helped us to sneak in. We had two late passes and one sleeping-out pass a week. I think the matron and sisters probably felt that they had some parental responsibility for us."

Lynette Richards-Murray's salary was "only £9 a month in my hand and out of that £9 a month I used to send home half of that and live on the other half. Being a civil servant in Guyana it sounded like a lot of money but I didn't realise they were going to take money out for taxes, superannuation, national insurance, boarding and lodging. You know you had to let it stretch. You didn't have to buy food but of course you needed things like stockings."

Student nurses drinking tea and eating cakes (Royal London Hospital Archives)

Caps, Uniforms and Discipline

The General Nursing Council for England and Wales,
23, Portland Place, London, W.I.

UNIFORM PERMIT

The General Nursing Council for England and Wales hereby grant permission to

MRS. *GLORIA GREGORIA FALODE*

whose name is entered on the General Part of the Register under Registration Number *362127* to purchase the Registered Uniform prescribed by the General Nursing Council.

Date *6.12.65*

M. Henry. SRN.

Registrar.

NOTE.—This Permit must be produced when purchasing the Uniform or any part thereof. The Uniform can only be obtained from firms authorised by the Council to supply it.
IMPORTANT.—This Permit must be most carefully preserved, and can only be replaced by Special Order of the Council.

Uniforms and discipline were an important part of the NHS in its early years and all new recruits had to respect them.

Before starting her training, Margaret Knight "had to buy these awful-looking shoes that were the requirement for King's College Hospital. I think they were called black Oxfords … specially built for nurses who have to be on their feet all day." She also remembers her nurse's uniform, which was "white and blue striped with a white apron and the caps, I think they were the laughing stock of the other hospitals around London; they were very peculiar looking caps. Second-year nurses were called 'kipper caps' because their caps were slightly different. They looked a bit like kippers! I think nurses' caps from other hospitals were a little rounder and flatter than ours. They were not very attractive looking and we had to wear stockings and ugly black Oxford brogues …

"Our chief surgeon was the Queen's surgeon, he had a voice like thunder. He shouted at me one day because my stocking seam was crooked. He stood at the bottom of the ward and I was going up the ward with a whole pile of bedpans and he shouted, 'Nurse with the bedpans, your stocking seams are crooked. I wondered if he thought I should throw the bedpans down and straighten the stockings! I just turned around and said, 'Yes sir, sorry sir.' A nurse was terrified of ward sisters and doctors."

Lena Hunt remembers: "Each hospital had a different design for caps, in which we took great pride. Discipline was certainly very different – for example, nurses never ever addressed each other by Christian names while on duty, and to call a doctor by his Christian name was a hanging offence! I remember being soundly told off for whistling on one occasion by the sister tutor – I was off duty at the time.

"She said, 'If you colonial nurses are going to behave like that I don't know whether we shall want to have any more of you.' Of course my reply was, 'Yes, sister,' as it had to be."

Tryphena Anderson was glad that nursing was a disciplined profession, "because back home we're used to a routine and discipline, so that was not a problem for me but sometimes it's hard to go by discipline when you have to remember who's senior to you and who to open the door for. No one wanted to do the sluice. If you were the junior nurse that was your job. If sister asked, 'Have you cleaned the sluice?' and you said 'Yes' and you had not, you would clean it tomorrow and any other jobs you had not done and as a result you would leave late."

Margaret Knight recalls that "the ward sister she was really a dragon, she did not like what she termed 'colonials', it didn't matter if you were from the Caribbean, Canada, Australia or wherever. She thought we were beneath her and she tended to crush anyone who came from the Commonwealth. She kept referring to me as, 'You little colonial'. It was awful. So I had a rough time on that ward."

Encountering patients

Playing bingo in Robinson ward, Mile End Hospital c1972-79 (Royal London Hospital Archives: ME/P/8)

Most of the Caribbean recruits had good relationships with the patients, although sometimes there could be difficulties. Neslyn Watson-Druée remembers "being invited into homes and primarily patients' relatives' homes. I remember patients used to say things about me and relatives used to invite me home and I would be invited out for tea and so on. I was a very caring person. There was one staff nurse who took a particular liking to me and she also invited me to her home. I think she was rather pleased with me because I was fresh."

Sherlene Rudder recalls that "some of the patients were very nice. I can remember two at that time. There was a lady with a lot of children and she used to talk to me and say, 'I don't know how your mother could let you go so far from home.' On the other side, I was on a ward, I was making and helping someone pass the teas out and this man said, 'You have to watch these darkies you know, they'll steal the milk out of your coffee.' I froze. I was glad my father was not around to hear. In our district stealing is considered a disgrace. I felt really cold. I withdrew within myself from these people if this is how they would think. Years later I realised that man was very insecure, nobody had asked him anything, he needed to be noticed. What I found then and compared it, the people who are most ignorant are the ones who have never been abroad."

Allied Health Professionals

Some Caribbeans joined the NHS as allied health professionals, working as carpenters, cooks, porters and auxiliaries. Some, like Derek Harty, found initial experiences a bit overwhelming.

Daisy Anson went to the Sherwood Hospital, looking for work. "They sent me to the laundry and there I got the job … The man who was there said the pay was £5/2/6p. I was walking on air coming out! I worked on the calender, the machine we used to draw the sheets through. You had to put the sheets in, roll it round and then press it down. The other girls at the back put the sheets in and we would take them out and fold them. My hours were from 8am until 5pm. I was 37 years old. There were other workers from Jamaica and all over. I enjoyed it."

When Derek Harty first arrived he worked in a factory with his mother and then applied to work in the NHS, in a laboratory. "I got a job eventually in 1966 at East Ham Memorial Hospital in London … My first job was as a junior technician. I can remember the first duty I had was to take blood. When I saw blood being taken, I didn't feel good at all. I actually fainted! I was wondering if I could continue doing jobs like that. After the first day it got easier. From the very first day I was among a team of people who made me feel comfortable and I was looking forward to studying for my new career. I was given day release: one day a week I would attend college and my fees and fares were

paid for … I remember my salary was not … more than I was getting in my job in the Banana Board in Jamaica. I didn't mind, I saw progress in the job. Staff were wonderful and we still meet and speak together. It was like a little family, it was a small hospital."

Initially Nelson Auguste "worked in hotels, factories and building sites even as a gravedigger. There were only two of us and then one Friday, I buried so many people I was frightened and I packed the job up! A friend was working at the National Heart Hospital and they said to me there are vacancies and I went there, filled out a form and got the job. I started work in 1972 at the National Heart Hospital in Westmoreland Street. My first job was a general porter."

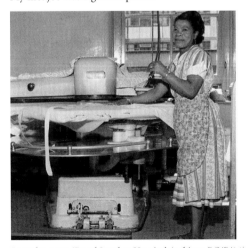

Laundry press (Royal London Hospital Archives: BG/P/14)

Occupational therapy attracted Elizabeth Yates because "it sounded interesting and it was people-oriented. The course was a three-year programme. A third of it was on clinical placement in different hospitals and the rest of it was college based. Within the college base you had academic studies, for example anatomy, physiology, medicine and surgery. We had to learn different occupational techniques like needlework, drama and woodwork, weaving and pottery. It was good."

Siburnie Ramharry joined the NHS to be a dietician. She lived in the hall of residence and made friends with two fellow students from the Caribbean. "The first part of the training was fairly general, we did basic nutrition. The course was run in such a way that anybody who didn't want to do the dietetics could stop and maybe go into catering and hotel management. We did very strange things in our first year like how to do laundry and the correct way of folding napkins. We did a lot of cookery and needlework. The second part was much more concentrated on nutrition, dietetics, we had to do a lot of biochemistry and psychology because obviously you were working with people. I really enjoyed it and it actually began to make sense."

Inez Stewart worked in a cutlery factory when she first arrived in Britain, but then "a hospital job came up at the Northern General Hospital, where they wanted people to work in the dining room so I applied and got it. [It] was a big hall where

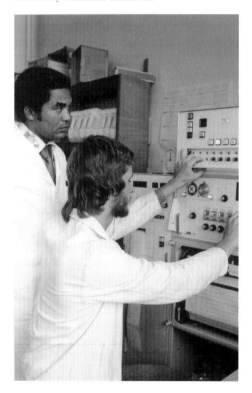

Derek Harty (left) photographed for Medical Laboratory Technician Handbook

hospital staff had a meal and there was a kitchen downstairs where they sent the meals up in the lift and you had to serve and collect the meals, wash up, dry and clean up afterwards. I was the only Caribbean worker there."

Olivine Benjamin was 18 when she joined the NHS as an auxiliary. "It was looking after patients and you did everything except medicine but you had to undertake all the roles that the nursing staff did. The staff were very friendly … There was an Italian lady who adopted me as her niece, she's still my auntie! Then a white lady who was my mum! … They really did look after me. We had two weeks' training when you first started; they showed you how to make beds and things like that. There was a group of us who were just giggling, so they got fed up and said, 'You there, you there,' and that was the training. It was a geriatric ward. We used to do 30 baths per week, Monday to Wednesday was bath day and you were assigned to a certain ward each week and the routine never changed, you knew what you had to do … It was very hard work … we had a patient who never used to put his feet on the floor and we used to get him up in the morning and get him to the side of the bed and he used to sit there and two people had to lift him bodily to get him in the chair and then at night he would just get up and get back in bed. He would never get out of bed and he did that for years! We had no training in lifting patients."

Hazel Watson found her first few weeks at Leavesden Hospital "a bit frightening … because I had never seen anybody have a fit before and seeing people fall on the floor and shaking. I was really petrified. I soon got used to that." She comments that fortunately, because she had younger brothers and sisters, she was working with children.

Caswell Jeffrey applied to work as a carpenter at the General Hospital, Birmingham. "I saw somebody and he said, 'oh yes, we need a carpenter.' We went and saw the foreman and he wasn't too impressed by a black man, from the West Indies, asking for a carpentry job in this country. He asked me if I was in the union, and I said 'No', and how I knew about the job and I said 'I saw it in the paper' … We went across the yard over to a next building and he told me to stay outside … I could hear he was saying to the person that a black man is outside asking for a job. It ran through me, what chance do I stand? The door opened and they said to come in and when I got in the man just got up and shook my hand. I was surprised. He asked if he could help me and I told him I saw a job advertised and I am a carpenter, he said, 'Yes there is a job going here.' He asked where I was working and about the wages I was getting, he said he couldn't afford that money here but if I need the job it's here for me. So he asked when I could start and I said Monday … It was general building, repair and making anything new … The hours were 48 hours, that was the basic hours, then Saturday afternoon to Sunday all day that was overtime. I worked with the first person that I saw when I went in on the Monday and … he took me under his wing. I think he needed a bit of experience about black people, he started to ask me a lot of questions and things like that, but he was quite a nice person."

Doctors and Dentists

Dr Eddie Adams joined the NHS to do research work at King's College. "There were other students from the Caribbean, one was working and one was a student. I was homesick for home all the time. As soon as I was qualified I got my first job in the NHS at King's College Hospital in 1964, but at the end of 1963 I was doing locum work for King's College. I did casualty and venereology. I was anxious to work. I was feeling good. It was 8 to 12 hours per day and I was paid £8 to £12 per month."

John Parboosingh found the training process "very similar to what I'd left in high school in Kingston and the standard of education in Kingston at the time was extremely high and so I didn't get any shocks at all. I felt quite comfortable and quite confident in my ability to learn.

"The first year was very much classroom and laboratory work. By the second or third year it was anatomy, physiology and biochemistry, so this was more human orientated. Patient contact started in the fourth year … Nurses and physicians were extremely kind to us. I think I had no experience of prejudice. In fact I think those who came from overseas including other Commonwealth countries in those days were very well looked after."

Like her husband, Jean Parboosingh found that lecturers treated the Caribbean students very well. Patients too "when we were training were very

helpful to students and were very pleasant to us."

Dr Stanley Moonsawmy was "very anxious and apprehensive in the beginning because I didn't know what to expect in the educational system. One or two students were very accommodating

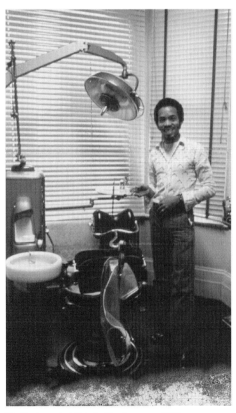
Dr Eastmond at Trinity Road surgery, 1975

and they would approach you and ask where you're from and start a conversation.

"A few became quite friendly … but the vast majority in my class were either middle or upper class and sort of looked at you as an odd foreigner in the class and rarely socialised with me. There were one or two exceptions … a young English chap from Lancashire and he had come up in a trade union family and had a more wider view of the world rather than the old empire colonial view. There was a very active West Indian student association including a West Indian calypso band, cricket teams, so those of us like myself who played cricket had social and sports activities of our own."

Dr Victor Eastmond worked as a London Transport guard for a year, then decided he would pursue his initial desire to go into dentistry: "I did a course in radiography at the Royal Free Hospital in London and was offered a job at the same facility when training was completed in December 1969."

Dr Anthony Lewis describes himself as 'trailblazer' because there were no other Caribbean students on his course. However "after that year … a lot of Caribbean students started to come and all of them started to look to me as a big brother. … The first year I did physics. In 1963 I actually entered the dental school itself and I got my first diploma, from the Royal College of Surgeons of England in November 1967."

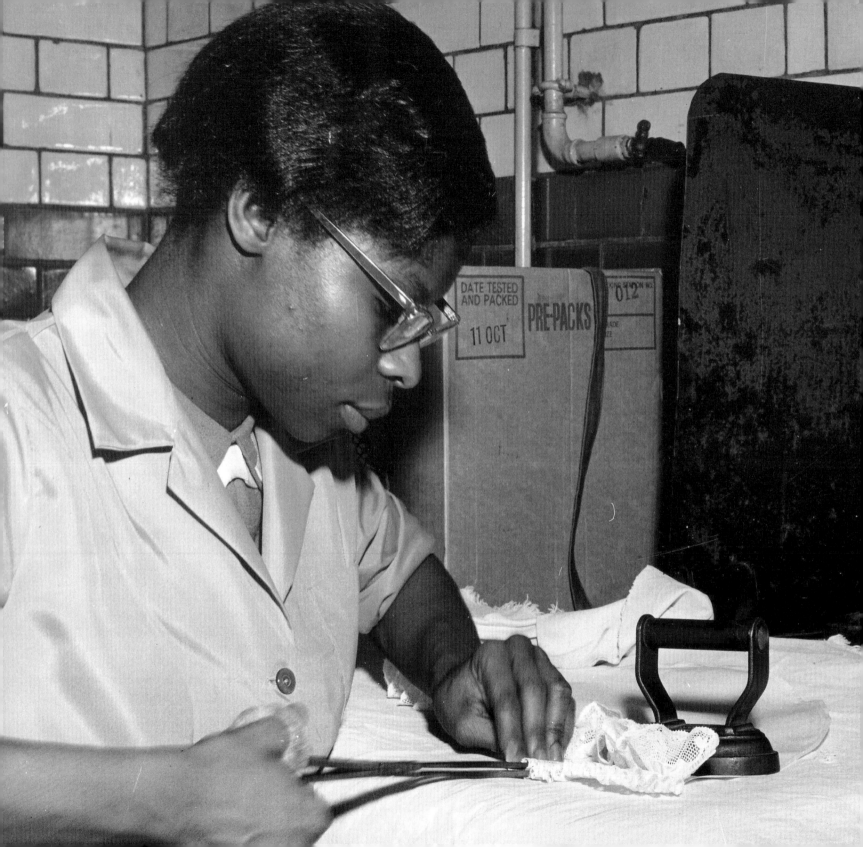

Getting on in the NHS

Caribbean nurses and other health practitioners have mixed stories to tell about their career development in the NHS during the early years. Most completed their initial training, qualified, and went on to do further training so they could move into more specialist and challenging fields of work. Many received help and support within the NHS. But there were also many – particularly, but not only, in the nursing profession – who felt that because they were from the Caribbean, they had to overcome discrimination and prejudice. However, despite the difficulties, Caribbean health professionals progressed through the NHS, sometimes making history on their way.

Laundrywoman goffering sister's lace cap with goffering iron and tongs, London Hospital, Whitechapel, 1960s (The Royal London Hospital Archives: LH/P/2/33)

"A positive experience"

Caribbean health professionals were trailblazers, providing role models for the next generation of BME health workers. Starting from the early years, they progressed through the NHS into positions of enormous responsibility. Some achieved high-status positions.

Lena Hunt "worked at St Paul's Hospital until I had my first child in 1956. For a short period I worked at a local health centre until we moved to the north east in 1966 where I worked at Darlington Memorial Hospital until we moved once again to Runcorn, Cheshire in 1979. I did 'bank' work in 2 or 3 hospitals in Chester, but then I got a permanent part-time job at Halton General Hospital outpatients' department, where I stayed until I retired in 1992. It was a very positive experience. Many times, like many others, I would say I was going to give it up and never be a nurse again, but I never did, and always came back to it somehow. With reference to the many nurses of different nationalities who staff our hospitals nowadays – it was ever thus. While I was in Harrow, I remember the nurses' dining-room had small tables which seated four. There were hardly ever two nurses of the same nationality at any one table. There were nurses from Greece, Nigeria, Java, Ireland, Germany, Sierra Leone as well as the Caribbean. I never particularly wanted to be in management. I always wanted to do 'hands-on' nursing, which is what I did all my years. I was also able to do that and fit it in with family commitments. So it worked out quite well."

Nola Ishmael first took up a staff nursing post and was later "encouraged to train as a health visitor". After four years as a health visitor, "my boss came to me and said she wanted me to take over a bigger clinic ... In 1987 I applied for the job

Dr Nola Ishmael awarded first prize for efficiency in 1972 at Whittington Hospital

of assistant director of nursing … I didn't think I would get the job but being short-listed was good enough for me … I told my secretary to cancel any appointments … because I would not be shifting until Greenwich rings … the phone rings and a voice said, 'Am I speaking to the newly appointed assistant director of nursing?' I just whooped with joy … You didn't have black assistant directors of nursing." Later she became the first black professional private secretary of the Chief Nurse of England. "There were no books to show me what to do … I seized the opportunity for a number of reasons … as a career progress [and] … because I wanted to show other black nurses that opportunities exist beyond aspirations."

Thelma Lewis left psychiatric nursing and qualified as a laboratory technician. She worked at St Paul's Hospital, Coventry, covering "five aspects of medical technology, histology, haematology, biochemistry, bacteriology, parasitology … From there I went to St George's Hospital, Hyde Park Corner in 1958 to 1968 as a technician and went up to senior grade. You had to go to the wards to take the blood and you tested them depending on the level you were at. I also did antenatal clinics and blood transfusion work. It was a very wide field. Then I spent some time in the Eye Institute of Ophthalmology from 1968 until 1970. Then they called me back at George's and I went to the Royal Dental in Leicester Square from 1970 to 1984 and did haematology there until the age of 50

when I took early retirement." She thinks that "Maybe because people from the Caribbean are very adaptable and open-minded about things; if one door closes another one opens … All was well with the hospitals that I worked because at that the time the students from Africa used to come over to write their exams, although their work was of a similar standard over there. So one could see fellow black students ahead of me because they came to write their finals."

Having qualified as a dietician, Siburnie Ramharry worked at St Mary's Hospital, Paddington, then felt the time had come to move up. She thought of specialising in paediatrics, "with children on special diets … also St Mary's had a renal unit and I used to cover that, dealing with special diets for renal patients and dialysis as well. So it was quite an exciting time to be at St Mary's … I applied for various jobs and one very nice dietician who worked at St George's said, 'Why are you applying for a senior 1 job, you're really more experienced than this.' I stated I had been abroad and I didn't really know what I should be aiming for. So she invited me to come and have a chat with her and she suggested that with my experience in Bermuda I could now apply for manager's jobs.

"A job came up with the Liverpool Health Authority as a dietetic manager and I was successful in getting it, they wanted someone to build up their community services. I really enjoyed

it. You arrive in Liverpool from Bermuda thinking, 'What am I doing here and I can't even understand their accents.' I think somebody asked, 'Why did you apply for the job in Liverpool?' and I said, 'it was because that's where the Beatles came from, so it can't be all bad!' I really loved it there and it was quite a large area to cover. I started in 1980 and was there for about eight years."

Nelson Auguste progressed from general porter to theatre porter and supervisor "I liked to work in that hospital and enjoyed my job. I became supervisor because when you're dealing with patients you had to be careful and there were Spanish and Moroccans who couldn't speak English properly so it was felt best that I took the job because sometimes you might take the wrong person to theatre; especially blood, plasma and oxygen, you've got to be careful not to use the wrong thing. I used to prepare the patient, make sure the gloves, oxygen were ready and if the patient arrested everything is prepared on that trolley. There were Dominicans, Trinidadians and other people from different islands as well as other nationalities at the hospital.

"I became a shop steward because I was a union member and the present shop steward was a chef and they decided he was not on the staff's side but on the management side. So they nominated me and that was it."

Breaking through discrimination

Many Caribbeans encountered discrimination in the early years of the NHS but with single-minded determination went to great lengths to break through the barriers, so achieving their own goals and setting role models for those who followed.

Lucy Martin-Burnham qualified as a midwife and then went into health visiting. She had to find her own accommodation, which was difficult because she was black. Fortunately her tutor organised it for her. Lucy worked for two years in England and then returned to Jamaica for a while as a public health nurse. Coming back to England, she "saw a job advertised in Berkshire … got the interview … and they said, we can offer you a job as a district nurse midwife but not as a health visitor, it is not customary for them to have colonials as health visitors. I then said could you tell me where I could get information to find other places because I'm prepared to try … I decided to apply to Berkshire County Council and then I was called for an interview and I was very, very pleased because the county nursing officer and medical officer of health were friendly and welcoming. He said 'we welcome you with open arms and welcome colonials.' I was obviously the first black person in this particular area but I didn't feel daunted. It didn't take long in a rural setting for word to get round … I was very pleasantly surprised when I visited people, they would say

with a welcoming smile, 'Oh do come in, we have heard about you' … They were very, very nice people."

Having worked for a year, Neslyn Watson-Druée "went to see a senior member of staff and told her of my aspirations that I wanted to be trained as a health visitor and she actually said to me that 'health visiting wasn't for black girls.' I decided that I was going to prove her wrong. It seemed as if I was in a catch 22 because I was now still on a student visa and I asked her to revoke my visa and she wouldn't revoke my visa unless I stayed at the hospital as a midwife. I wanted to train as a health visitor so I thought how on earth can I do this? I decided the only way I could get myself out of this trap was if I were to buy property … At the time … when you saw places for rent, they would say, 'No Dogs, No Blacks, No Irish' in that order … So I saw a maisonette and it was going for £9,500 at the time … I went to the GLC to the housing department and told them I wanted a 100 per cent mortgage. The person laughed at me … I wrote directly to the director of housing at the GLC. I said that I was a midwife and that I had aspirations to go on to do my health visiting training but more importantly in the here and now I am giving very valued service. I walked out of that office with a 100 per cent mortgage … So l left midwifery and was accepted by Merton, Sutton & Wandsworth Area Health Authority, I was sponsored for health

visiting training. I went to the Polytechnic of the South Bank and there was a cohort of 52 of us and of the 52 there were 50 whites and two blacks."

Louise Garvey remembers that the early years in the NHS were "good because people sort of got on and supported one another", but that both patients and staff could be racist. Despite this, she set her sights on becoming a sister: "I did extra training, whatever was going in the hospital. Opportunities were always there for nursing but at the same time there was the racism and the feeling at the time that nurses should only be there to do the bedside things. You put yourself forward to ensure that whatever internal training is being offered you get on board … I used to do what I called the watching game. I would watch and see what training was available, who was going for it and how often. I used to challenge the situation. I would say nurse A and B and whatever, she's had x amount of training, I haven't been on one. This training is available and I am interested, here is my application and that's how you got on these things in those days. You had to fight for them."

Lynette Richards-Murray "went to an agency in Bristol and they said to me, 'I'm sorry but we don't take your sort of people.' That was in 1963. They wouldn't get away with that now." She went on to become a district midwife. "In those days if you wanted a house and a car you became a district midwife … I went to Redhill and worked as a midwife there and went to Croydon and worked for seven years as a district midwife. After that I could see there were things I wanted changing within the system. I would go to my boss and I was doing teachers' courses and so on. They were saying, 'We can't give you the time off you have to do it in your own time.' So I did it in my own time and paid for those courses. I thought, 'I need to try my hand at management.' In fact, I wanted to become a health visitor … I applied for a job in South London and they said they didn't take black people, we don't think the people would accept you, that sort of thing. I got my first nursing officer post in Greenwich District Hospital in 1973. I was there for four years. I was in charge of all the gynaecology and the antenatal services. I went there and implemented continuity of care and things like that. I must have had a good reference because I saw this job going as a senior nursing officer at St George's, Wandsworth. They must have liked what I said at the interview."

Joyce Bleasdille-Lumsden's matron supported her decision to do SRN training: "She was leaving the hospital to go to Colindale Hospital in London and she said to me, 'Follow on from me and when you finish your training you wouldn't need a reference.' The tutor of the student nurse training … wanted me continue with the student nurse training because I used to come first. He advised

me to take the General Nursing Council test and said they would like to keep me to do my student nurse training in the group, but the nurse tutor was from South Africa and we learned that she didn't like black nurses … she was encouraged to take me and I came first in all my exams. I did my combined training for BTTA (British Tuberculosis and Thoracic Association) and SRN (State Registered Nurse) with Edgware. I got on very well with the patients, having done chest nursing in Grenada I got used to tuberculosis patients.

FACE THE FACTS

IF YOU DESIRE A **COLOURED** FOR YOUR NEIGHBOUR

VOTE LABOUR

IF YOU ARE ALREADY BURDONED WITH ONE

VOTE **TORY**

The Conservatives once in Office, will bring up to date the **Ministry of Repatriation,** to Speed up the return of home-going and expelled immigrants.

Racist election literature from the 1964 British general election. Pic courtesy of Lambeth Library

The nurses were mainly from Malaysia and China and I got on well with them. I went to do my SRN training in Edgware Hospital until 1966. From Edgware I went on to do my midwifery training at Luton Maternity from 1966 to 1967. I got married and had a break, did a little agency work. I was at the Royal Northern as ward sister until 1974. I had problems getting to work on time and at night time getting home, so I thought the district nursing would be much better. I applied to St Thomas's Group … and I was accepted and started in 1974 as a community sister."

Caswell Jeffrey, in his position as carpenter, soon showed that black people could work as well, if not better, than whites. "The people I worked with were a bit cautious for a black person to come in and expected that perhaps I didn't know the job. Of course I didn't prove them wrong they proved themselves wrong. I could remember that myself and another man were hanging some doors. Of course I was a young man and he was much older, I wasn't trying to show him up, I did mine well before him and one of the blokes that was coming from the engineer shop perhaps didn't think that a black man could hang a door! When he passed and saw that I hung the door, he didn't go where he was going, he turned back and before long a lot of them surrounded me and I couldn't even move! I remember that."

Introducing innovations

Caribbean workers made their mark on the NHS – not just in terms of hard work and commitment, but also in other innovatory ways.

Elizabeth Yates progressed through the NHS to become head occupational therapist at the Royal Northern Hospital, at which point, "I started making history because I think I was the first black person to get that level of post." She made history in other ways too. "In 1972 I saw a job advertised and thought, 'that sounds like fun.' They were looking for a head occupational therapist to commission the occupational therapist service at Northwick Park Hospital and Clinical Research Centre. I got the job. It was a steep, fast learning curve for me … you had to validate assessment tools and be totally objective in what you were doing. In 1974 we commissioned the physical rehab department. In 1976 we commissioned the psychiatric unit and started the paediatric service. There has always been a shortage of occupational therapists and one of the things I did in the late 1980s was I dropped a note to regional personnel and said, 'you know, if we are all having problems, why don't we do regional recruitment overseas?' I think I must have been one of the first people to go overseas to recruit staff … We advertised in France, Germany, Denmark, Sweden and Norway … We managed to get one occupational therapist for each district. I think some of the changes that came around made me look at how I was using

staff. I became much more aware that I had a multi-ethnic and religious group and we needed to look at things like Eid, Jewish and Muslim holidays etc. I felt that it was important that we respected that but as a department we celebrated with everybody, which was fantastic."

D Anson was the first black person to work in the canteen at the Nottingham City Hospital: "I cooked for nurses, doctors and other staff. The staff were good and if anybody came of my colour who was looking for a job, they would call me in the office to see if they should hire them. Sometimes we cooked for 200 or 300 people, only two of us, just the chef and I … Sometimes they asked what to cook, but they didn't really have a menu, so you just cooked what you wanted … Wednesday I said to the chef that I'm going to cook curry lamb and rice and I cooked it. When the man that came for the doctors' dinner brought back the dishes, he said to the chef, the doctors who were Indians said, 'Compliments to the chef' and that it was 'the best dinner they ever had!'"

Derek Harty remembers there were not that many people from the Caribbean working as laboratory technicians at that point. "I trained under a person from the Caribbean at East Ham Hospital and we had a very good relationship. I spent eight years at East Ham Memorial Hospital.

"After my A levels I decided to go further. I took the higher national certificate in biomedical sciences specialising in chemical chemistry; that

was a two-year course. I was successful in achieving that. After that I became a registered laboratory scientist. I still pursued my academic career in further qualifications and I achieved the fellowship of the institute. I took the special examination to qualify me as a fellow of biomedical sciences in 1973.

"At East Ham in 1973 I decided to apply for a senior post and there was not one available for me. The pathologist who had previously worked at East Ham Memorial Hospital he came to work at Whipps Cross Hospital and I asked him if there was a senior post there. He said, 'Yes, there is.' So I left to go there. In fact when I was offered the job at Whipps Cross, East Ham did offer to upgrade me but I wanted to see new horizons and experiences. I spent about 10 years in my senior post and was successful in getting a chief technician's post. Then about 10 years ago I got the post of technical manager for the biochemistry department and this is the post I have until the present day."

Work and children

Caribbean women in the health service often had the double burden of combining work and children. Some had support from sisters and matrons; many had reorganise their working patterns, often working night shifts.

Tryphena Anderson remembers: "One of the things you didn't do those days is get married because they didn't have married people in nursing. Even after you finished your training it was hard to get work in the NHS at the time. I left in 1954 and I had a baby and then I started again at Grantham Hospital. Then I had my second baby while working at the same hospital. To continue nursing I had to find somewhere that would take me with two children and allow me to live out, as approximately 98 per cent of nurses were required to live in. I met this lovely lady who was working at a psychiatric hospital called the Coppice, which was affiliated to the Mapperley Hospital. She told the matron who then said, 'I can only take five students, if they pass their exams I could have a place.' Well I've never prayed for somebody that I did not know to pass so much! Come November, I'll ask, did they pass? No! Then I had to pray again! ... I was successful in the end and started at the Coppice in 1958. Even at Christmas, you had to work. Do you know Christmas is the hardest time for someone to look after your children? This Christmas I had to work and I went to matron and I said, 'Matron, I would love to work, but I haven't

anyone to look after my children. Could I bring them to work?' She said, 'Yes Nurse Anderson, of course.' She was so nice." Tryphena Anderson subsequently applied to the Nottingham City Hospital to do postgraduate training, qualified as a midwife and was later accepted for a year's course in health visiting training, "the first black person on a bursary in health visiting at that time."

For Erena Kydd, "the only way to be with the kids was to go back into nursing so I started doing nights in 1965 at Amersham Hospital for 11 months and I then transferred to Booker Hospital in High Wycombe. It was a cottage hospital for the elderly. I worked as an auxiliary in the evenings. The duties at that time was to do the washing, take the patients out of their beds, give them a bath and dress them. To me I felt as if because I am a

Muriel Bussue at Lodge Moor Hospital paediatric ward, 1974

foreigner and I'm black I was the one who was disadvantaged because every dirty part belongs to me and nobody else. So I had to keep on doing the dirty work and I felt to myself, I shouldn't be doing it more than the others they should take a part in it as well. You had to do everything as a trained staff, put in catheters etc, but the pay was bad, for the whole month it was £25. We auxiliaries never got a raise. The majority of auxiliaries were from the Caribbean."

Louise Ghartey decided to move into physiotherapy and started in one of the satellite hospitals of St Thomas's as a junior physiotherapist. "It was an odd position because it wasn't the type of hospital where a newly qualified physiotherapist would normally want to work but due to the kindness of the principal of the school who had heard about my demise of my stillborn baby, she offered me this job and I was extremely grateful. This was a job where I worked primarily with patients who had polio. You were on call and you had to work during the week and weekends. I worked at St Thomas's for eight months and from there I applied for a job in a small general hospital called St James's in Balham, which has now closed. I started as a junior physiotherapist but while there I was promoted to a senior physiotherapist in less than a year. I worked there until September 1973, I had my first child and stayed at home until the beginning of 1974. It was extremely difficult fitting in the hours with having a small child and taking

the child to the nursery and collecting him. So I was looking for something that allowed me some flexibility and a job came up in Wandsworth for a community physiotherapist and because St James's was part of the Wandsworth Health Authority I was successful in getting that job. It was a wide-ranging job with patients. I worked there until 1978. It was difficult to get any other jobs in terms of seniority because the next stage up would have been superintendent. In 1978 I had my second son so I stopped working for a while and resigned my post. I then saw a job with St Francis Hospital in Dulwich, which was an elderly care hospital attached to King's College, there was a deputy superintendent post. I applied and got the job. We had students and junior members attached to us, teaching to be done and managerial tasks. I was there until 1983. From 1983 to 1991 I worked in Tooting Bec Hospital as an assistant superintendent physiotherapist."

Hazel Watson took time out to have children. "I spent about two years or so at the hospital I then got married in 1959 and had my daughter … I looked after my family and I didn't work again until 1964. I worked at Guy's Hospital. I was a domestic housekeeper in the evenings … My duties were bringing the patients their meals, filling up jugs of water, washing dishes, getting the trolley ready and sending it back to the kitchen. My husband was a carpenter so he would come in and take the kids. I worked in that position until the early 1970s."

Doctors and Dentists

Like nurses and other allied health professionals, Caribbean doctors and dentists also had mixed experiences of getting on in the NHS. Some were consistently successful; in other cases, discrimination caused problems.

By the end of 1963, Dr Eddie Adams "was doing locum work for King's College. I did

Dr Eddie Adams aged 25 when a student nurse at Guyana Public Hospital, Georgetown

casualty and venereology. I was anxious to work. I was feeling good … From there I worked in Lambeth Hospital, doing surgery, and from there I was attached to St Thomas's Hospital doing surgery again. I was a surgical houseman. You do minor operations and assist the registrar and consultant doing the big operations. It was urology and general surgery in Lambeth Hospital and at St Thomas's Hospital it was ear, nose and throat surgery. I found it very good and I was well taught. I was at Orsett Hospital in casualty in Essex for one year and from Orsett back to Albert Dock Orthopaedic Hospital in Alnick Road for two years. I worked as a senior house surgeon in obstetrics and gynaecology at King's College Hospital. I then worked at Chertsey and Acton hospitals as a casualty registrar for two years each. From Acton I went to do general practice in Clarence Avenue, London."

John Parboosingh "did house jobs in Edinburgh and then my first obstetric house job … I did the house jobs right up until June 1966. By this time I had applied for this job in the Royal Infirmary … Then I was promoted to a lecturer position and worked for two years. I became a senior registrar in the Royal Infirmary. It was absolutely fantastic; it was a fantastic learning environment, very practical and also lots of positive feedback … You worked with individuals for many, many years so that you could benefit from role models. I became a senior lecturer with

senior registrar status and then was appointed as senior lecturer with consultant status at the Royal Infirmary of Edinburgh in 1972 … I started to focus on obstetrics … and developed a regional programme in a high-risk clinic in a very low socio-economic area of Edinburgh called Sighthill; the obstetrics clinic is still going today. I also set up similar clinics in the Borders … we selected Sighthill because it had the highest perinatal mortality and morbidity rates … we now have several of these clinics coming out of the Royal Infirmary … I was the youngest consultant to be appointed in the Royal Infirmary." Ultimately, Dr John Parboosingh decided to live and work in Canada but it was a difficult position because "one felt so comfortable and we were so welcomed in Edinburgh and there was nothing in my job at the time that I was unhappy about."

Jean Parboosingh married and then "did three house jobs, one was at Chalmers Hospital in Edinburgh for six months, the second job I did was in obstetrics in the Elsie Inglis Hospital in Edinburgh and the third was a locum house job in gynaecology at the Royal Infirmary. I became pregnant in my last job and in those days you didn't take on another house job or as a registrar if you were having a family. So I stayed at home for approximately six years having three children … when I decided to go back to work after raising three children … I decided to go into general practice. Well that was an experience that I really appreciate to this day – including doing house calls. In fact I probably had many of the women, small children and the elderly patients in the practice requesting my care. The geriatric patients often seemed to gravitate to me as I was the only woman doctor in the practice."

Dr Stanley Moonsawmy worked as a locum at a local hospital in Edinburgh, but "in those days sometimes it was difficult for foreign graduate students to get the top posts as young junior doctors in the teaching hospitals. You often had to go peripherally to the country hospitals miles from Edinburgh. I was a houseman in medicine in Galashiels, which is about 40 miles from Edinburgh and that was a six-month post followed by six months of a surgical houseman's post at Bangour Hospital in West Lothian, which was about 10 or 12 miles from Edinburgh. Thereafter I moved back to the teaching hospital as a senior house officer and slowly rose to being a registrar in the main teaching hospital, which was the Royal Infirmary, Edinburgh, where I spent two or three happy years while doing my postgraduate training in my chosen speciality, respiratory diseases. I continued to practice in the hospital system in this area until about 1973 and then found it difficult as I had reached what was regarded in those days as the ceiling for non-white doctors. In that it was very difficult to get the young registrar grade."

Dr Moonsawmy was advised to emigrate but, having married, he decided to go into general practice in the UK. Of that time [1973] he says: "there were a lot of stories in tabloid newspapers about foreign doctors in Britain often in a stereotypical, rather derogatory way … Most of us had to go into single-handed practice which was much more strenuous and much more difficult but enjoyable at the same time. That is how I ended up a single-handed practitioner since 1973 to the present time … In this area of Edinburgh, there were no non-white consultants at all when I was a student and young doctor, and the first non-white student appointed in Edinburgh had to be in the specialities where white doctors did not want to go into, such as the venereal diseases clinic, psychiatry or geriatrics. None of these attracted me as I wanted to specialise in respiratory diseases.

I ended up in a village just on the edge of Edinburgh, which was a mining community … I did encounter problems in my first one or two years here … Quite a few of my patients heard that it was a foreign doctor and disappeared completely by registering with other practices. So that meant I had to inherit a practice with less patients and therefore of course with less income, but over the years I've built it up and won the respect of the local population by hard work, extremely excellent work and the word spreads around very quickly in communities if you set certain very high standards and you keep to them. Difficult at times, but one has learnt how to survive."

Dr Franklyn Jacobs had always intended to return to the Caribbean. "I was offered a partnership at every practice where I worked. My answers were always the same: 'No, I will be going back home.' That was, until I was 'bitten' by a surgery in Hornsey Road, North London, not too far away from here. In fact, I have never roamed far and Hornsey has remained my medical constituency. The principal of the surgery where I did locum work had advertised for a partner. He

A framed picture of Dr Eddie Adams

Many rivers to cross

indicated [that] he was interested in me applying. I gave my usual spiel that I was heading home back to the Caribbean [and] he encouraged me to speak with my father [who] was, at the time, a practising GP in Bradford … When given the details of the offer my father had no hesitation in convincing me to stay remarking that the offer of a partnership and the terms were excellent. I remember him saying 'You're a very lucky boy' … I remember

Dr Victor Eastmond receiving 1977 NLS Hope Award

being totally undecided and having a headache over the enormity of the effect of my decision. My whole life was about to change. Needless to say, I succumbed and accepted his offer. I officially began working as a partner within the National Health Service on 1 April 1977. April Fools' Day! And so, here I was, a foreigner, a West Indian, working within a predominantly Greek surgery where most of the patients and all of the staff were of Greek or Greek Cypriot descent. As such, it was necessary for me to have an interpreter with me during my consultations. It was a truly exciting time, which I enjoyed immensely. About 18 months after officially joining the practice, I remember looking at myself in the car mirror while driving to work one morning and thinking 'My God! I'm really enjoying my work. I was born to be a GP.' I have enjoyed my work ever since."

Dr Victor Eastmond was offered a job at in the radiography at the Royal Free Hospital in 1969. "I spent about three months there before leaving to do freelance agency radiography at many hospitals within the National Health Service. I continued this work in the NHS until 1970. It was a very challenging profession in that I was called out to various hospitals to examine patients, take their X-rays at the request of doctors who diagnosed and prescribed the treatment that was necessary. I must say having done the radiography course at the Royal Free Hospital … my desire became even greater to carry on and to try and achieve my

dental requirement. I decided to do some more A levels during that period of time. I had to do those at evening classes and ended up with a total of four A levels, which gained me a place at the Royal Dental Hospital in London. I started that course at the age of 25 in 1970. I then did the four-and-a-half-year course which finished in November 1974. I gained two degrees, the bachelor of dental surgery (BDS Lon) and degree and licentiate of dental surgery of the Royal College of Surgeons of England degree (LDSRCS Eng) in January 1975. I then started to do oral surgery as a junior house surgeon at St George's Hospital and the Royal Dental Hospital for three months each in 1975. I had to work every other weekend on-call when I was at St George's Hospital. So it was a very hard time as far as the commitment … It was however a very great learning experience … I was also a senior house surgeon at the Edgware General Hospital later in that same year."

After his training, Dr Anthony Lewis went on be a senior house officer at the Leeds Dental Hospital. "I worked there until 1971 when I passed the final fellowship examination. I got on extremely well with the patients. Well, I was senior house officer from December 1968 to December 1969. Then I was appointed registrar in dental surgery at the Leeds Dental Hospital in 1970 and during this time I was successful in the fellowship of dental surgery of Royal College of Surgeons of both England and Edinburgh."

Improving chances for others

Through their work in the NHS, many Caribbean workers worked to improve life chances for other black people in Britain. Neslyn Watson-Druée worked in Brixton as a health visitor. "I went into Brixton and I had very mixed emotions because I saw young women like me with no prospects, who had possibly one or two children but living in very cramped and cold accommodation, deprived areas and I used to think. 'My God!' you know. I learnt a lot, I found it very distressing I remember I used to walk along the street with tears running down my face when I saw the condition in which people lived. I remember going back to the college and saying to my tutor, 'I cannot do this.' I identified very closely with black people and they weren't like me, and I don't want this reported wrongly, but I went through a stage where I was ashamed of being black, because of what I was seeing and what blackness represented in Brixton at the time. I had to come through that and I am so grateful for that tutor who was wonderful. She said, 'Neslyn, you have to understand economics, you have to understand racism.' I said to her 'racism, what's that?' I did not know what racism was. I came out of that being proud to be black. By standing there I wanted to improve the life chances of black people as far as I can."

Louise Garvey remembers: "There were a group of us who were always about cultural diversity and you had people who were anti it, so we were sometimes seen as troublemakers. But as far as we were concerned, if you are saying treat each individual as an individual, and if you've got individuals coming from different cultures, then most of the time, they weren't informed … If it was good for the European, it was good for everybody else. So a lot of us had to fight to get things in place and of course that didn't make us popular. Dietary care that took ages to come on board, skin care that took ages to come on board, communication even now there's struggles with that. That was one of the main ones. Of course

Louise Garvey (with husband) presented with a community services award by her local mayor and mayoress, 2001

you've got people coming from the Caribbean, they've got different accents, you've got your French patois, Creole and what have you. A lot of people still believe in their mother tongue and they go in and they might be in pain and they communicate and because people didn't

Sherlene Rudder accepting the MBE for her work in genetics, Buckingham Palace, 1995

understand and weren't willing to listen and they were impatient."

Sherlene Rudder qualified as an SRN in 1967. She planned to go into midwifery and then return to the Caribbean but "as I got into it, home seemed further and further away. The patients were very friendly. A baby I delivered was named after me, so there's a child somewhere in Southampton called Sherlene! I left Southampton as a qualified midwife and I opted for health visiting in 1971 and was sponsored by the London Borough of Brent. So I arrived in Harlesden. I think that's when I really came into my own and found my niche. I liked the combination of health issues and the teaching … the opportunity to help out on social issues. There was dreadful housing and poverty. We had an enormous case load but there was such a tremendous spirit amongst the team of health visitors. The fact that I stayed as a health visitor for 16 years must have been positive. The work was tremendously hard but it was varied and I liked relating to individuals. I met so many individuals with sickle-cell anaemia, which I didn't have any experience of at all. I felt, as a black public health worker, I would have to do something about it because they were just coming down the corridor with an enormous amount of problems. I worked in a health centre with an enormous amount of GPs who didn't know anything about sickle."

After qualifying, Denzil Nurse worked as a staff nurse. "At that time I was aspiring to the nursing officer's post … One of the things that impacted on about 16 of us at the time was a statement that one of the senior officers remarked to one of our nurses. He said, 'I don't know how the staff would react taking orders from a black man.' One or two of my other colleagues had similar remarks made. We analysed that situation and thought there is no progression here." Denzil Nurse came out of nursing but went into community development work in Huddersfield. "By that time there was a very large African-Caribbean community in Huddersfield and I … saw that there was quite a bit of work to do in developing different projects, like setting up a day nursery for mothers … setting up day care for the elderly, and other projects linked to Social Services." He believes that the British Council "had mentored us well in the early days but didn't protect us from any abuse and that is something I would want put in place now – a mentorship programme for any young person going into the NHS, so they are not disillusioned and you can pre-warn them that they are likely to come into these situations. Having said that, people are different these days. In the past you got 65 per cent of the people being abusive, it's reversed now; it's about 5 or 10 per cent. As they have become used to working alongside black people, understand their culture, interacted within the community, people do not see them as a threat anymore."

Chapter 6
Achievements

The people who contributed to this book are proud of their achievements, and rightly so. They have achieved a great deal from personal satisfaction, through to the implementation of policies and initiatives that have benefited the NHS in general and black nurses and BME patients in particular. Most of them stayed in Britain after their training, and worked for the NHS until retirement. They overcame enormous challenges – including discrimination – to achieve within their fields and progress into specialist fields, in some cases becoming the first black person to do so. Some took their NHS experience and expertise abroad, developing important health initiatives in the Caribbean, Canada, and Africa. All of them played a vital role in the first twenty or so years of the NHS. They helped to ensure that the new health service worked as well as providing key role models for BME health practitioners to follow.

Student nurse receiving award (Royal London Hospital Archives)

Personal satisfaction

Many people in this book mention personal satisfaction and a sense of having done worthwhile work as among their most important achievements.

Today Dr Neslyn Watson-Druée leads the Kingston Primary Care NHS Trust. She is "enormously proud of what I've achieved and the key to those achievements have been courage, drive and tenacity … The NHS is a brilliant place to be. You can excel in human resources, science, nursing, medicine, administration, information management and technology, and the list goes on … In the whole scheme of things, it is almost as if there has been a guardian angel there guiding me all the time because all of those experiences have actually come to shape the woman I am. It is those experiences that have made me such a positive advocate. When I'm actually saying to people out there in the Health Service, 'Yes, racism does exist, and you too can overcome it. I have.'"

Denzil Nurse was a psychiatric nurse in the NHS for 23 years, as well as working with his local community in Huddersfield. Recently, he has also worked on community initiatives in Gambia. He says his achievements "include recognition for my community work and Gambian newspaper coverage for community initiatives in Gambia." For him, "my life's work was around people. In nursing it was about caring for people and … I have fulfilled that aspiration … Generally speaking, my work in the Health Service has been

a positive experience. I think the negative experiences only served to build my character. You take the rough with the smooth and make the best of your life … the experience of coming to Britain and working in the NHS has given me enormous satisfaction tinged with one or two unfriendly situations. I have never let them override or blot out what was a fantastic experience."

Tryphena Anderson pretty well achieved all she wanted, although she does have one regret: "The positive side is, thank God, not all people were prejudiced and against the advancement of black people. I did everything I set out to do but one thing I wanted to do was wear the cream uniform of the Jamaican health visitor. I would have loved to have had that job in Jamaica."

For personal reasons – children and a divorce – Margaret Knight was not able to continue nursing. She worked for a while in administration and then returned to Barbados. She is "sorry that I could not go further with my nursing and complete it. I would have liked to become a qualified nurse." However, she achieved much in a secretarial career and also became a writer. She is "proud of what I have achieved. I have learnt from my … short career in the NHS a great sense of responsibility and discipline and I have been able to use this discipline in my life and with my children."

Lena Hunt says she "never particularly wanted to be in management. I always wanted to do 'hands-on' nursing, which is what I did all my

years. I was also able to do that and fit it in with family commitments. So it worked out quite well. I think there is as much difference between nursing now and nursing then, as there was between Florence Nightingale's nursing days and nursing in the 1950s … Many of us went into things blindly and came up with a nice romantic idea of what nursing was about. Would I do it again? The answer would be yes!"

Mrs Daisy Anson worked in hospital canteen departments until she returned to the Caribbean in 1975. "In the cooking line I was the only black person until I got my cousin," and her cooking talent earned her popularity and respect with both staff and patients.

Derek Harty considers he "more than fulfilled my career aspirations. When I started out in the job I didn't think that one day I would be managing the department. The key to my achievements, I would say, is hard work and to be a professional at my job and in my attitude. I have found my profession very rewarding. I'm still finding it exciting. I think with any career you choose, you've got to have some passion and love. Once you've got passion, you'll get by."

Thelma Lewis took early retirement from the Royal Dental Hospital and went on to further her academic achievements. She taught for a while in Tanzania and then went to St Vincent, where she does voluntary work with the parish. She says, "I have learnt from my career that people need

Neslyn Watson-Druée MBE, 2005

people. We are all brothers and sisters, some are more fortunate than others … I see working in the NHS as a noble profession … It is the satisfaction that you give, the love and support to the patients and the entire team who are responsible for the welfare of the sick. The joy that I receive if I'm just walking down the street and somebody remembers me and says, 'This used to be my nurse, she took my blood,' you get that inner joy for the service you rendered."

Nelson Auguste took redundancy in 1994 just a few months before he was due to retire. Of his career he says, "My experiences were very good because nurses, doctors and porters, everyone had someone to help them who was there before in their training. They would show you what this is, where it has to go, how to file x-rays and notes. I wouldn't mind getting a job there again if I had to … You have to be very brave to be a porter because when somebody dies you have to take the body to the mortuary. I even took royalty to the theatre!"

After a successful career in dentistry in Britain, Dr Victor Eastmond returned to Barbados, where he set up his own practice in St Michael's.

He says, "I regret not doing dentistry earlier because I love it and I always feel good. I would like to share this philosophy with everyone where people say if you enjoy your work it is no longer a job and you can therefore understand why I do not consider dentistry to be a job. It is just a love."

Helping others

Several of the interviewees mentioned the satisfaction they gained from helping others and putting patients first. Many would agree with Leila Ghartey, who retired in 2004, having reached the position of senior physiotherapist at a large mental hospital in Surrey. "I enjoyed my work so much I thought every day was a positive experience. The majority of the people I saw as patients were all people that needed help and I felt it was a positive experience to give these people treatment that made them better."

Having started her NHS career working in the dining room in the Northern General Hospital, Inez Stewart went on to be a nursing auxiliary. "They used to say, 'Just go with that nurse and see what she does.' I did not get any training at first. I was making beds, giving them drinks and so on. I was working full time from 7.30am to 4.15pm in a mentally ill, mixed geriatric ward. When they moved the patients in the community into houses I continued caring for them. I am happy with what I've done … if I knew then what I know now I would have gone into training as a nurse, but I've enjoyed my work. I love to help people. What made my job rewarding was seeing the long- and short-stay patients come into the hospital ill and caring for them until they are well enough to go home."

Olivine Benjamin worked in the NHS as a nursing auxiliary for 34 years; due to a back injury, she retired in 2004. "Overall, I am happy with what I've achieved. The key to my achievements has been caring for people less fortunate who can't help themselves. I really enjoy looking after people. I've learnt from my career to be patient and understanding."

Dr Eddie Adams, who set up his own surgery in about 1977, says, "the key to my achievements has been I look after my relatives, I'm the last of eight, they're all dead now. I looked after them when they were ailing and that gave me satisfaction. I learnt to help people. I could retire tomorrow but when people ask you to see them and look after them … That's how my career was."

Despite many challenges, Dr Stanley Moonsawmy achieved a great deal. Of his medical career in the NHS he says, "Overall my experiences have been very interesting, rewarding and fascinating. I am full of job satisfaction in that I still have families of four generations and I now see children that I actually delivered who are now in their twenties and thirties working in this area." The keys to his achievements include "determination and a degree of stubbornness" and his determination to beat racism by being "excellent and better than your white compatriots." "I've learnt lots of things in my career. I have learnt to be a good communicator with not just officials and management but also with patients. I've learnt from patients how they communicate and think, what their fears and pleasures are, how they approach a doctor and their expectations … that gives you immense satisfaction in your job."

"I ENJOYED MY WORK SO MUCH I THOUGHT EVERY DAY WAS A POSITIVE EXPERIENCE. THE MAJORITY OF THE PEOPLE I SAW AS PATIENTS WERE ALL PEOPLE THAT NEEDED HELP AND I FELT IT WAS A POSITIVE EXPERIENCE TO GIVE THESE PEOPLE TREATMENT THAT MADE THEM BETTER." Leila Ghartey

Being the first

Nola Ishmael progressed through the NHS to become the first black assistant director of nursing, then director of nursing and finally the first black professional private secretary to the Chief Nurse of England. She wrote policies, met government ministers and helped to set standards in nursing. Of her achievements she says: "In 1998 when the NHS was celebrating 50 years I was selected as one of 50 women who nurses in the NHS said had inspired them. This came as a real surprise and in 2000 I was awarded an OBE when I was still at the Department of Health and an honorary doctorate from the University of Central England in 2003."

In 1972 Elizabeth Yates was appointed head occupational therapist at the Royal Northern Hospital, becoming the first black person to achieve that level. Describing her achievements, she says, "the majority of it has been positive ... we had the odd patient who refused treatment from a black occupational therapist and I must admit my policy was, occupational therapists were allocated to specific areas and anyone could refuse treatment but once they refuse treatment, they refuse it. If they didn't want to be treated by her then they were refusing treatment." She took up a post as lecturer at Brunel University, where she was the first black lecturer in occupational therapy.

Later she joined a steering group, run by Neslyn Watson-Druée, to run a career management development programme for occupational therapists and is still committed to creating a black occupational therapists section within the profession. "Within my health profession there were very few Caribbean occupational therapists. Within the wider thing of the National Health Service, you would find the Caribbean women in the catering and cleaning department. As one of the more senior people from the Caribbean in the hospital I always felt that they supported me and I thought that I had a responsibility to them, which they paid back ten-thousand fold. You know it was little things; I always felt if there was a cleaner from the Caribbean, the room got an extra shine."

Elizabeth Yates was appointed head occupational therapist at the Royal Northern Hospital

Making changes

Many Caribbeans used their work in the NHS to implement important changes and initiatives, some of which were aimed at addressing the health needs of BME patients, who had previously been ignored. In some cases, NHS-trained Caribbean health practitioners took their expertise back to the Caribbean, or to other countries.

Through her work as a health visitor with Berkshire County Council, Lucy Martin-Burnham was able to "assess health needs and respond as I deemed appropriate and as a result I was able to organise the following initiatives: the first mothers club, the first playgroup, the first home-help service, the first childminding service, the first invitation for husbands to be present at delivery, first menopause group, first discussion group on childcare and parenting from 0-5 years old."

Gloria Falode progressed through the NHS to reach the post of nursing officer. She retired in 1994, but "in 2003, someone suggested I do the assessor's course where I can assess NVQ students. I feel I have come full circle [and] have been doing this since October 2004 … The key to my achievements has been determination … if you've really chosen something and you feel that is what you want to do I think you should really strive to be the best at it."

During her nursing career, Muriel Bussue worked with infectious diseases, spinal injuries and cancer patients. She worked for seven years with

Lucy Martin-Burnham's general nursing certificate, December 1954

the "mentally ill as a nurse" through a charity called Anchor, which was partially NHS funded, and still does voluntary work in her community. She says, "I have learnt from my career that if you decide you want to do it and work hard enough,

you can make it. Sometimes I think if I had my time different I would have done nursing first and then had a family, but on the other hand when I see what my children have done and how they have helped me, for example, one would take me and fetch me from work. I couldn't have had the benefits that I had if I had done it in a different way."

Lynette Richards-Murray worked her way up the NHS to become a director of nursing in South London. Among other achievements, she implemented the practice of keeping nursing mothers and babies together. She says, "If you want things done you've got to work hard for it, you can't just sit back and up to now I'm still like that." She took early retirement in 1992 but "thought there are a lot of things I want to do and began to concentrate on Guyana and found they had no deaf services. I went to the Department of Health in Guyana and said, 'I can't promise you anything but I will go back to the UK and see what can be done.' So I linked up with the Commonwealth Society for the Deaf. In 2000 we got a full service for Guyana. In 1987 a group of us working in health services in the Caribbean formed a group not only for nurses and midwives but for allied professionals as well. We have been instrumental in helping with cancer care, and getting medical equipment in Guyana. AGNAP is a wonderful organisation … I am very proud and I am very thankful for the guidance my parents and especially my father gave me because he was my guiding light … When he was very ill and I went back to look after him I was then a director of nursing and I hope he was hearing what I was saying. I said, 'Dad I'm a director of nursing!'"

Sherlene Rudder's achievements include starting a "support group in Harlesden for people who had sickle cell … There were so many families and youngsters with problems. We decided to go to America, Elizabeth Anionwu and myself, where we learnt an important lesson. The first sickle and thalassaemia centre was opened in Brent at Willesden General Hospital … OSCAR [sickle-cell research organisation] started the whole sickle-cell movement going really … I received an MBE in 1995, which shocked and amazed me that I should be considered for that type of award. It was a wonderful day and I met a lot of people in the palace who were enormously proud of me when I got there. My award was presented to me by the Queen herself. That was fun!"

Both Professor John Parboosingh and Dr Jean Parboosingh had distinguished medical careers in Edinburgh. John Parboosingh initiated pioneering work in obstetrics and gynaecology at the Royal Infirmary. In the late 1970s, they moved to Canada. John Parboosingh became professor at the University of Calgary, and then went to Ottawa to focus on e-learning and research. He says, "the reward of practising medicine in Scotland remains very positive. I have patients who still write to me." Jean Parboosingh joined Health Canada as a medical consultant and says, "the training I had years ago has given me the opportunity to do a variety of things that many other people couldn't do."

"IF YOU WANT THINGS DONE YOU'VE GOT TO WORK HARD FOR IT, YOU CAN'T JUST SIT BACK AND UP TO NOW I'M STILL LIKE THAT" Lynette Richards-Murray

Speaking for black nurses

Many Caribbean health professionals worked to achieve improvements for other black health workers or to highlight their situation. Louise Garvey did so: "When I went into nursing I didn't have any health problems but ... most of us came out with bad backs because in those days they didn't have the lifting equipment, the laws weren't about. Most of us – and I can speak for black nurses – most of us have bad backs! Key employment law and NHS policies have improved situations and it has enabled me, and a lot of other black nurses, to make the necessary changes for care. A lot of what we've done in the early days we've seen them put into place in government policies. So we're pleased about that. A lot of those policies that have happened have come about because we as black nurses helped to enable those situations. I felt that enough wasn't being done about highlighting the contributions of black nurses. I can only speak for Nottingham. I got Millennium Award funding and was successful in producing a little booklet and it's called *Nursing Lives of Black Nurses in Nottingham.*"

Whittingham Hospital
Management Committee
Preston

Training School for Nurses
This is to Certify that

LOUISE ZELPHYR TAYLOR

having been duly trained in Psychiatric Nursing at Whittingham Hospital has satisfied the Examining body of her Proficiency.

This ____ 2nd ____ day of ____ MAY ____ 19 68

Frederick Phipps Chairman of Management Committee.

D V Williams Matron.

Louise Garvey's certificate for training as a psychiatric nurse, Whittington Hospital, May 1968

Giving back to the community

As well as highlighting the needs of black health workers, many Caribbean nurses and health workers achieved important initiatives by taking their expertise and commitment back into their communities, either in Britain or the Caribbean.

Joyce Bleasdille-Lumsden achieved the position of community nurse and took early retirement in 1993 on health grounds. She says: "My experiences have been positive I think because I got on well with people and I always put my patients first and think of my patients as myself. I think it's my upbringing that has been the key to my achievements. My mother … was the lady who used to look after children in the village with marasmus and kwashiorkor … When she died 9 March 2000, I gave a bursary in her name to the child who comes first in my village in the common entrance every year for 10 years. So far six children have got the bursary. They get $500 so they can spend it on books, clothes or whatever they want for their education."

When Erena Kydd started at Booker as an auxiliary, there was no union organisation: "Eventually, we got started with a union but it was only a name, it wasn't for staff. When I left Booker my wage was just £6,000 a year. I left there in 1992 … When the grading system came in you were supposed to get a pay rise but auxiliaries didn't get anything. I got my pay rise by taking the hospital to court." She has since worked on many

Joyce Bleasdille-Lumsden accepting an award

initiatives, "including the High Wycombe & Buckinghamshire branch of the Commission for Racial Equality for some years. I was on the executive board for about five to six years. I was also school governor and turned that school around … I worked on the elderly being accepted in council houses and homelessness. I worked on police training for about 2 years … I gave lectures on what is good and not good for racial equality. I currently work for the blind. The key to my achievements have been the things that I've worked on and I can see the benefits now, it's coming back to the people and what I've learnt I'm giving back to the community."

Siburnie Ramharry achieved the position of senior primary care dietician. "When I started I was a community dietician and now I'm a primary care dietician, but I'm still doing the same thing … I think some of the smaller professions are just not well known and slightly invisible … Schools need to push with Caribbean children to show that there are other opportunities rather than nursing."

Hazel Watson achieved the position of supervisor of domestic staff, a post she held until retirement in 1998. Since then, she has "been involved with a community group for young people".

Dr Franklyn Jacobs has run a single-handed practice since 1982. In addition to this he "sought other ways of making a contribution to my community, hence my involvement in the African

Caribbean Medical Society (ACMS). The ACMS was founded by me, Lord Pitt and Dr Eddie Simon in an attempt to fill a gap within the medical establishment … We felt that there should be a

Dr Franklyn Jacobs, 2005

society through which black doctors (of which there were few at the time) could liaise so as to form a base from which black medical issues and health education could be promoted and championed. As founders, we each desired to give something back to our community." He was also the first president of the West Indies UK Group and would like to see West Indian GPs invited to work in Britain, particularly in the inner cities.

Dr Anthony Lewis achieved the post of registrar of dental surgery at Leeds General Hospital before returning to Jamaica in 1971, where he became the first dentist appointed to the Bustamante Hospital for Children. In 1999 he became director of dental surgery for Jamaica and retired from that post in 2003. Previously, he had been president of the Caribbean Atlantic Regional Dental Association.

Among his achievements, he mentions the work he did in Leeds with young black people, trying to ensure they received a proper education. He says, "I only got good responses and feedback from the patients that I saw and I learnt so much working in the National Health Service. I personally have no regrets at all and only good things to say. I know that if I had stayed in the UK I would have had the opportunity to do much more but for 20-odd years I was really on the cutting edge of providing remedial maxillo-facial and oral surgery to the people of Jamaica and in that context I think I did very well."

Hard-working West Indians

Caswell Jeffrey worked as a carpenter with the NHS for about 32 years. He says, "I enjoyed carpentry and that's why I stayed in it all my life. That was my training and what I wanted to do ... The workforce if we are talking about the hospital, there was quite a number of West Indians but they were mainly women and they worked in the domestic department and I was the only black man there at the time and I had to go in all different departments and I have seen them working and I tell you they worked really hard. In those days you didn't have the polisher or anything like that and I was always in sympathy with them. What they had was a huge block of wood with a handle underneath that was a piece of blanket, they put the polish on the blanket and that's what they pushed on the floor to polish the floor and it was always the wooden floor, nothing like it is now with lino or tile. It was very, very hard work. I knew the West Indian people, they came here and worked very hard in the Health Service." He describes his achievements as "hard work and determination."

PAY AND ALLOWANCES	HRS/SESS/UNITS	RATE	AMOUNT
BASIC PAY	40.00	177.00P	70.80
WEEKDAY O/T	3.00	177.00P	5.31
SAT.O/T	6.00	177.00P	10.62
BONUS	13.00	140.58P	18.28
SERVICE SUPP			0.66
SERVICE SUPP	9.00	1.65P	0.15
TOOL ALLOW			0.50
ROUND UP C/F			0.42

SAL SCALE & OCC. CODE: A62000 003	OFF SCALE DIFF	INC. DATE	COMM. IN GRADE 290463	COMM. IN UNIT 290463	COMM. AT AUTH. 290463

PAYROLL 4101 B'HAM AHA (T) CENTRAL DISTRICT 41 EMPLOYING AUTHORITY

METHOD OF PAYMENT 1 CASH | PAY PNT 01 | DATE 08 06 80 | TAX PERIOD W 10 | TAX CODE 0 259H | N.I. NUMBER 2856 B

C JEFFREY

PAYROLL NUMBER   01

PERSONAL NUM.   01 01047

AMOUNT PAID   80.00   ****

TOTAL PAY AND ALLOWANCES   106.74

DEDUCTIONS (— INDICATES A REFUND)

INCOME TAX 15.60 | NAT INSUR 5.09
U C A T T 0.55 | GENDENCLUB 0.10
OVRPAY.B/F 0.91

| GROSS IN THIS EMPLOY 1071.61 | TAXABLE PAY TO DATE 1026.32 | TAX TO DATE 157.80 | L D | CUM. N.I. EE. 51.30 | CONT. OUT N.I. 35.80 |
| TAXABLE PAY IN PREV | TAX IN PREV | SUPER. TO DATE 45.29 | L | CUM. N.I. EE | CONT. OUT N.I |

SPN   4.49   TOTAL DEDUCTIONS   26.74

PERSONAL NUMBER 01047   AMOUNT PAID   80.00

Payslip of Caswell Jeffrey, 1980

Look back:
Photographs
from the age

*Pharmacy technician prepares equipment
in the hospital pharmacy, London
Hospital, Whitechapel, May 1968 (Royal
London Hospital Archives: LH/P/2/55)*

Below: Celebrating Christmas on a ward at Bethnal Green Hospital, 1960s (Royal London Hospital Archives: BG/P/14) *Right:* Student nurse receiving training certificate, Bethnal Green Hospital, early 1960s (Royal London Hospital Archives: BG/P/12)

Many rivers to cross

Hazel Wigmore, clinical teacher, instructing pupil nurse Mabel Corbin on dispensing from the drug trolley on the ward, London Hospital, Whitechapel, c1967 (Royal London Hospital Archives: LH/P/2/55)

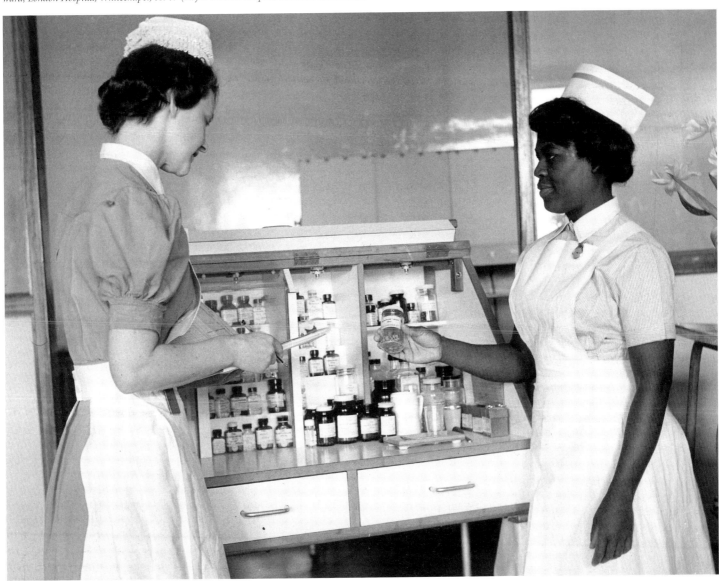

Top: Playing bingo in Robinson ward, Mile End Hospital
c1972-79 (Royal London Hospital Archives: ME/P/8)
Above: *Nurses greeting Frederick Angel, 14 April 1962*
Right: *Caring for the elderly,*
Robinson ward, Mile End Hospital, c1970
(Royal London Hospital Archives: ME/P/8)

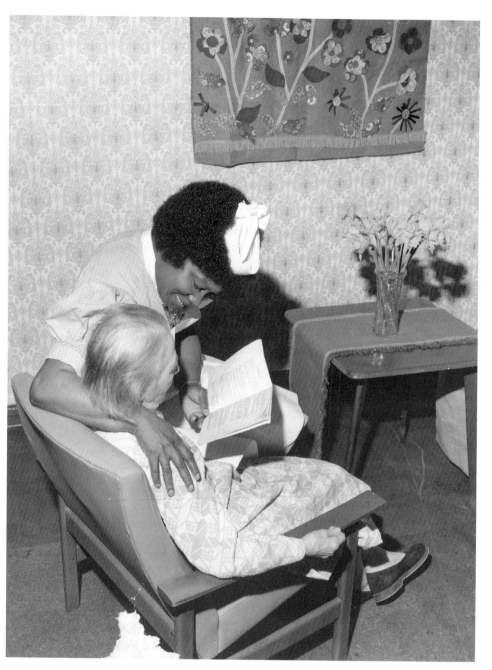

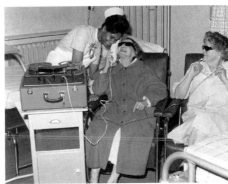

Left: Cafeteria at Mile End Hospital, 1972 (Royal London Hospital Archives: ME/P/4)

Top: Auxiliary nurse assisting a patient at St Clement's Hospital, Bow, c19/0s (Royal London Hospital Archives: SC/P/8)

Above: Student nurse and patients at Mile End Hospital using audiobooks, April 1968 (Royal London Hospital Archives: ME/P/22)

Right: A pharmacy technician sterilises bottles with a sterile saline solution in the autoclave, London Hospital, Whitechapel, May 1968
(Royal London Hospital Archives: LH/P/2/55)
Below: Hospital porters, London Hospital, Whitechapel, May 1977
(Royal London Hospital Archives: LH/P/2/57)
Bottom: A children's Christmas party, Bethnal Green Hospital, 1960s
(Royal London Hospital Archives: BG/P/14)

Many rivers to cross

Laundryman working in hospital laundry, London Hospital,
Whitechapel, 1960s (Royal London Hospital Archives: LH/P/2/33)

Chapter 7: Look back

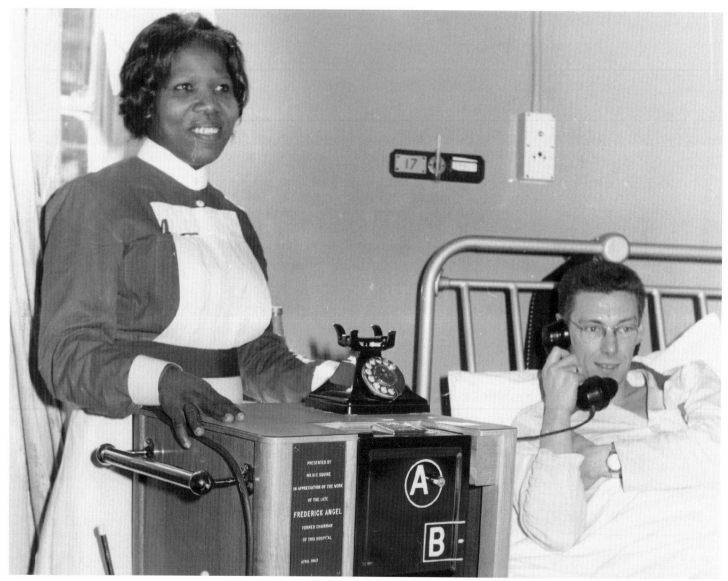

*Sister and patient using portable telephone, Frederick Angel Ward, Bethnal
Green Hospital, 1960 (Royal London Hospital Archives: BG/P/5)*

Many rivers to cross

Enquiries desk in the outpatients department, London Hospital,
Whitechapel, early 1960s (Royal London Hospital Archives: LH/P/2/53)

Chapter 7: Look back

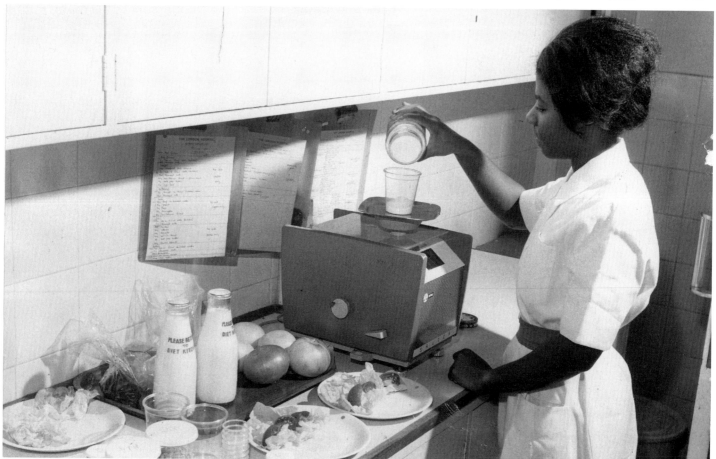

Student dietician accurately weighing food for research purposes, London Hospital, Whitechapel, 1968 (Royal London Hospital Archives: LH/P/2/24)

Left: Student nurse receiving training certificate, Bethnal Green Hospital, early 1960s (Royal London Hospital Archives: BG/P/12)

Below: Student nurse receiving prize, Bethnal Green Hospital, early 1960(Royal London Hospital Archives: BG/P/12)

Bottom: Bethnal Green Hospital: award of training certificates and prizes to nurses, early 1960s (Royal London Hospital Archives: BG/P/12)

Chapter 7: Look back

Chapter 8

The Modern-day NHS:

Making a positive difference for people from all communities

Diversity in the NHS

As this book has shown, in its early days the NHS drew on the inspiration and commitment of heroines and heroes from the Caribbean. The current NHS also has its fair share of champions from the Caribbean and other parts of the world. What has changed is that while the early NHS was based on the principle of universal provision for all, the current NHS has a more explicit commitment to equality. A central principle of the NHS plan, published in 2000 as a blueprint for major investment and reform, is that the NHS of the 21st century must be responsive to the needs of different groups and individuals within society, and challenge discrimination on the grounds of age, disability, ethnicity, gender, gender identity, religion and sexual orientation.

This chapter identifies some of today's champions – Cecile Day, Surinder Sharma, Carol Baxter, Barry Mussenden, John Batchelor, John James, Yvonne Coghill and Joyce Higgins – and their views of the modern-day NHS. They emphasise the NHS's commitment to a service that is fair to patients and staff from all communities and they confirm that people from Caribbean and other minority ethnic backgrounds have, as in the past, an important role to play in today's NHS.

It is fitting to begin with Cecile Day MBE. Cecile works in the Department of Health and is the chair of the department's ethnic minority working group. Cecile has been the prime mover behind this book and project-managed it from start to finish. In doing so, Cecile has demonstrated significant resolve and determination. For Cecile, this book is the story of a community, made up of many individual stories, of which only a few can be told here, that speak of all those from the Caribbean who contributed their lives, energy, passion and commitment to the NHS. "It is a story of determination, setting out to find a new life very different from the old one. It charts the difficulties and survival of those who share their memories here, which are not marked by

Cecile Day (second from left) and her family, December 2005 on the day of her investiture to receive her MBE

career success but continued endurance, fortitude and dignity. It is a story of the contribution made by those who made the journey and gave part of their lives to public service." Cecile adds: "These people's lives mirror that of the NHS, one of struggle and achievement, but most of all a dogged determination to make things better." Out of the these stories comes an important message – all the contributions in the past have paved the way for contributions now from the children and grandchildren of these adventurous travellers. Cecile believes that "the NHS, like British society as a whole, has changed for the better. However, it still needs the kind of contribution that Caribbean and other minority ethnic communities made in the past. It is an institution which belongs to all the communities it serves and we need to ensure its success by securing the opportunities it offers."

Cecile would particularly like to thank Sir Nigel Crisp, the former chief executive of the NHS and Permanent Secretary of the Department of Health for supporting her and championing the project.

Surinder Sharma is head of the Equality and Human Rights Group of the Department for Health and the national director for equality and human rights for the NHS. He was appointed in 2004; previously Surinder had worked on equality and diversity in a number of private and public organisations, including Ford Europe, the BBC and Littlewoods. Surinder says that it is vital for the Department of Health and the NHS to value the contribution that people from all sections of our society make to the healthcare system "It is imperative for the NHS to invest in a diverse workforce that has the skills and capacity to deliver a world-class service tailored to meet the needs of a diverse patient-centred NHS."

Professor Carol Baxter is head of equalities and diversity at NHS Employers, which was set up in 2004 to take over responsibility from the Department of Health for much of the workforce agenda, supporting and representing employers in the NHS. Carol has worked as a midwife, health visitor and health promotion specialist as well as holding senior positions in the NHS, the Department of Health and the higher education sector. Carol believes that "we need to promote model employment practices that support all staff in reaching their potential and respond to their different needs and preferences." NHS Employers has led initiatives such as 'Improving Working Lives' and 'Positively Diverse' to promote a more inclusive working environment, free from any form of discrimination and unfair working practices.

Surinder Sharma and Carol Baxter identify four reasons why the NHS should aspire to be a good and fair employer.

- First, there is an increasing legal requirement to do so from domestic and European legislation and case law.
- Second, from a moral standpoint, it is the right thing to do.

Carol Baxter

Surinder Sharma

- Third, there are sound business reasons. Most often, the NHS is the largest local employer and is in direct competition with other employers for talent. If the NHS is to provide the best patient care and customer service, and choice within those services, then quite simply its workforce must be the best and draw on, retain and develop the talents of all communities.
- Fourth, the NHS should act as a good corporate citizen. Nationally, the NHS is the single largest employer in England, employing over 1.3

million staff; it is also a major commissioner and procurer of services. With such economic muscle, the NHS has a responsibility, along with other statutory agencies to promote cohesive and healthy local economies

Carol Baxter stresses that "the NHS should be an employer of choice that successfully recruits, retains, develops and provides best-in-class flexibility as a good employer. There should be respect and dignity for all staff and their skills and abilities. There should be clarity and transparency in human resource processes for all employees, their managers and NHS organisations as a whole. Career and personal development must be fair and open to all, where everyone has the chance to progress and personal success is celebrated."

Barry Mussenden is a senior manager with the Equality and Human Rights Group. He joined the Department of Health in 2000, having previously worked on a range of grassroots black and minority ethnic projects across health and social care. Barry reflects on current staff numbers. "Over 170,000 NHS employees are from black and minority ethnic backgrounds. That represents over 14 per cent of the workforce, and is well in excess of the 9.4 per cent of the adult population in England from such backgrounds. These staff, working as nurses, midwives, health visitors, hospital and family doctors, allied health professionals and domestic and manual staff, provide vital clinical and support services to patients from all communities. Black and minority ethnic staff contributed significantly to the founding of the NHS. They continue to make a significant contribution."

As with the early years, there are still some barriers today, but slowly and surely these barriers are coming down. The statistics are encouraging from the boardroom to busy hospital wards to community health services. For example, about 7.5 per cent of NHS senior managers, including

salaried professional advisers who sit on NHS boards, are from black and minority ethnic backgrounds. Over a fifth of doctors working in hospitals and over 17 per cent of qualified nurses working in hospitals and the community are from black and minority ethnic backgrounds. What's more, these numbers have been growing steadily in recent years.

Mechanisms and schemes are in place to take legitimate positive action to help recruit more black and minority ethnic staff to the NHS and, once recruited, to help them stand a good but fair chance of progressing to senior positions. The 'Improving Working Lives' and 'Positively Diverse' initiatives, referred to above, are making a real and positive difference to the workplace. Alongside NHS Employers, the NHS Institute for Innovation and Improvement is also making a positive impact. As part of its management training schemes, the NHS Institute runs a 'Breaking Through' programme specifically designed to equip black and minority ethnic staff compete for senior NHS jobs. John Batchelor is head of the 'Breaking Through' programme. He started his NHS career with the ambulance service, where he worked as a paramedic before moving into management and senior management positions. John says "'Breaking Through' was launched in 2003. Since then, many participants – armed with confidence and insights into themselves and their organisations – have been successful in applying for promotion or

taking jobs or secondments to widen their range of experience for promotion in the future."

Programmes like 'Breaking Through' are important as, despite much progress among middle and senior management ranks, there are still only a handful of black and minority ethnic chief executives in the NHS. One of them is John James, chief executive of Brighton & Hove City Primary Care Trust. John, who has worked in a variety of NHS settings in senior positions, says that the contribution made by people with a

John Batchelor, head of the 'Breaking Through' programme

Barry Mussenden, senior manager with the Department of Health's Equality and Human Rights Group

Caribbean background to the early days of the NHS was "both immense and heroic." John looks forward to improvements in the health of people from black and minority ethnic backgrounds and to securing a much more diverse make-up of top teams in the NHS. Like Cecile Day, he believes that with determination, and by holding current NHS leaders to account these improvements can be made.

Mentoring can play an important part in helping black and minority ethnic staff reach their potential, particularly if mentors see mentoring arrangements as a two-way learning process. Yvonne Coghill, currently a nursing officer for external relations and communications at the Department of Health, speaks highly of the mentoring opportunity provided to her by Sir Nigel Crisp during his time at the department. In February 2004 Sir Nigel had issued his 10-point leadership and race equality action plan to the NHS. One of the challenges for NHS chief executives was to mentor a black and minority ethnic member of staff. Sir Nigel demonstrated his own commitment by recruiting Yvonne from Harrow Primary Care Group as his mentee for 12 months. Yvonne has not looked back since. She says: "I now have senior people in the NHS recognising my value and my worth, and nobody can take that away from me." Yvonne currently mentors four people herself, so that others can benefit in the same way.

The NHS Institute for Innovation and Improvement runs an on-line scheme called Net Mentor. Potential mentors and mentees can use

John James "It's about real determination."

Sir Nigel Crisp and Yvonne Coghill

Joyce Higgins, emergency medical dispatcher with the Greater Manchester Ambulance Service

Net Mentor to look for mentoring arrangements appropriate to their circumstances.

Job satisfaction plays an important part in most people's working lives. Joyce Higgins is an emergency medical dispatcher with the Greater Manchester Ambulance Service. Joyce came to the UK in 1966 from Jamaica. She has been in her current post since 1996. She encourages younger British Caribbeans to consider a career in the NHS. Of her own work, she says: "It is a challenging and rewarding job and a position where you know that you must be professional, remain calm, cool and collected, even when under extreme pressure. It is rewarding because you know that you have helped someone suffering in a distressed situation."

While this book is about NHS staff, it is fitting to end this chapter with Joyce's words. After all, making things better for patients, irrespective of their backgrounds, is the reason why people have chosen to work in the NHS in the past and will choose to work in the NHS of the future. It is the thread that binds current NHS staff, such as Joyce Higgins, to past champions such as Mary Seacole.

For more information about the equality and human rights group of the Department of Health, visit: www.dh.gov.uk/equalityandhumanrights
For more information about NHS Employers, visit: www.nhsemployers.org.
For more information about the NHS Institute for Innovation and Improvement, visit: www.institute.nhs.uk/nhsinstitute

Many rivers to cross

Author's Biography

Ann Kramer is an experienced editor and writer, who specialises in health and social history, particularly black and women's history. She has written or contributed to more than 30 non-fiction titles for adults and young people, including the best-selling *Woman's Body*, a health manual for women, *Human Rights: Who Decides?* and *Black Peoples of America*. Her father, Dr Thomas Kramer, went into general practice in North London within weeks of the NHS being established.

Appendix

	Country of origin	Date of arrival in UK	Age at arrival in UK	Means of travel	Profession
Eddie Adams, Dr	Guyana	1953	27	Ship	Surgeon
Tryphena Anderson	Jamaica	1952	19	Ship	Nurse, health visitor
Daisy Anson	Jamaica	1956		Ship	Hospital chef
Nelson Auguste	St Lucia	1960	20		Theatre porter, shop steward
Olivine Benjamin	Jamaica	1965	16	Plane	Nursing auxiliary
Joyce Bleasdille-Lumsden	Grenada	1960	23	Ship	Midwife, community sister
Muriel Bussue	St Kitts	1958	mid-20s	Ship	Nurse
Victor Eastmond, Dr	Barbados	1964	19	Plane	Dentist
Gloria Falode	Trinidad	1960	23	Ship	Nursing officer
Louise Garvey	Jamaica	1957	15	Plane	Nurse
Leila Ghartey	Guyana	1960	21	Plane	Physiotherapist
Derek Harty	Jamaica	1965	23	Plane	Laboratory scientist
Lena Hunt	St Kitts	1948	18		Orthopaedic nurse
Nola Ishmael, Dr	Barbados	1963	20	Plane	Nursing officer
Franklyn Jacobs, Dr	St Vincent	1974			General practitioner
Caswell Jeffrey	Jamaica	1960		Ship	Carpenter, shop steward
Margaret Knight	Barbados	1949			Orderly, administrator
Erena Kydd	St Vincent	1959		Ship	Nursing auxiliary
Anthony Lewis, Dr	Jamaica	1962	19	Plane	Dentist
Thelma Lewis	Guyana	1955	22	Ship	Laboratory technician, haematology
Lucy Martin-Burnham	Jamaica	1951	19	Ship	Midwife, health visitor
Stanley Moonsawmy, Dr	Guyana	1956	19	Ship	General practitioner
Denzil Nurse	Barbados	1963	19		Psychiatric nurse, community development
John Parboosingh, Professor	Jamaica	1957	17	Plane	Senior lecturer in obstetrics, gynaecology
Jean Parboosingh, Dr	Jamaica	1959		Ship	General practitioner
Siburnie Ramharry	Guyana	1962	19	Plane	Dietician
Lynette Richards-Murray	Guyana	1959	20	Ship	Director of nursing
Sherlene Rudder MBE	Barbados	1964	18	Plane	Midwife, health visitor, genetic counsellor
Inez Stewart	Jamaica	1960	21	Plane	Nursing auxiliary
Hazel Watson	Barbados	1957	16	Ship	Hospital housekeeper, supervisor
Neslyn Watson-Druée MBE	Jamaica	1969	19	Plane	Health visitor, lecturer
Elizabeth Yates	Guyana	1962	19	Plane	Occupational therapist

Healthcare is a challenging arena, but the opportunities are unlimited and the rewards boundless.

You could be working at the cutting edge of healthcare science or helping people cope with injuries, disabilities or emotional problems through your work as one of the many different kinds of therapists.

There are roles for technicians, managers, IT and health informatics specialists, even electricians and plumbers! There's not much you can do outside the NHS that you couldn't do inside it – and whatever you choose, you'll be part of the thousands of teams of people helping others to get back on their feet.

Whatever your age, experience and hopes for the future, why not consider joining the team in North Central London?

The North Central London Strategic Health Authority includes NHS organisations within the boroughs of Barnet, Camden, Enfield, Haringey and Islington. Visit the North Central London SHA website www.nclondon.nhs.uk and www.nhscareers.nhs.uk for information about the trusts in the sector, news on job vacancies and advice about NHS Careers.

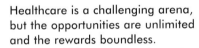

North Central London **NHS**
Strategic Health Authority

References

BOOKS

From Cradle to Grave: Fifty Years of the NHS: Geoffrey Rivett (King's Fund, 1997)

National Health Service: The First Thirty Years: Brian Abel-Smith (HMSO, 1978)

The National Health Service: The First Phase 1948-74 and After: Brian Watkin (Allen & Unwin, 1978)

Black Angels from the Empire: Judith Garfield (Eastside Community Heritage, 2000)

Celebrating Fifty Years of Women in the National Health Service (NHS, 1998)

Black British, White British: Dilip Hiro (Monthly Review Press, 1973)

Staying Power: The History of Black People in Britain: Peter Fryer (Pluto Press, 1984)

Colour Citizenship and British Society: Nicholas Deakin (Panther Modern Society, 1969)

Keep on Moving: The Windrush Legacy: The Black Experience in Britain from 1948: Tony Sewell (Voice Enterprises, 1998)

Roots of the Future: Ethnic Diversity in the Making of Britain (Commission for Racial Equality, 1996)

The Heart of the Race: Black Women's Lives in Britain: Beverley Bryan, Stella Dadzi and Suzanne Scafe (Virago, 1985)

A Chronology of Post-War British Politics: Geoffrey Foote (Croom Helm, 1988)

Twentieth-Century British Political Facts 1900-2000: David Butler & Gareth Butler (St Martin's Press, 2000)

PAPERS AND DOCUMENTS

West Indian Nurses and the National Health Service in Britain 1950-68: Linda Ali (University of York, MA dissertation, 2001)

Extracts from *Barbados Advocate* (1948, 1949, 1950s)

Extracts from *Nursing Times*

Staffing the Hospitals: An Urgent National Need (Government report, 1945)

Nursing Mirror (4 June 1965)

Nursing and Midwifery: Migration in Britain (*Nursing Times* Occasional Papers, 1 May 1969)

Extract from *Nursing and Social Change:* Monica Baly

Various Colonial Office, Ministry of Labour and other documents from the National Archives

Various Department of Health press releases taken from the internet (8 April 1998, 4 May 2005)

The Vital Connection: An Equalities Framework for the NHS

The Development of a Black and Ethnic Minority Health Policy at the Department of Health: Veena Bahl, 1993

Woman Health Officer (October 1958)

International Migration of Nurses: Trends and Policy Implications (*Global Nursing Review Initiative,* issue 5)

Black and Ethnic Nurses, Midwives and Health Visitors Leading Change: A Report of the Mary Seacole Leadership Award – the First Five Years (Department of Health, November 2000)

OTHER SOURCES

Mile End Hospital: student nurses' record of services and conduct: 24 March 1949 – 13 January 1953

Mile End Hospital: nursing student registers: 1 February 1962 – 31 August 1967

MH55/2157: Nursing recruitment

LAB 8/968: Recruitment of nurses from the colonies for nursing work in GB

CO 318/476/1: Recruitment of labour for Great Britain 1946-47

CO 318/487/4: Recruitment of labour for GB

PHOTOGRAPHS

Getty Images

East London Hospital

WEBSITES

www.movinghere.org.uk

www.blackpresence.co.uk

www.ccmacanada.org/urban/blackbrithistory

www.wikipedia.org/wiki/British_nationality

www.nhs.uk/England/AboutTheNhs/Default.cmsx

Acknowledgments

The publishers would like to give a special thank you to all contributors in the book for their time and patience in telling their important stories and to the many other interested parties who were not able to be included.

We would also like to thank for their assistance: Dr Nola Ishmael OBE, Barbara Brewster of the Barbados Overseas Nurses Association (UK), Rose Thompson, Caroline Oliver, Mr Owen and Mrs Karen James of the Jamaica Medical Association, Mrs Cynthia St Louis, Betty Why of the Association of Guyanese Nurses & Allied Professionals (UK), Mrs Hippolyte of the St Lucia Association (UK), Dr Marcia Barnes of the Jamaica Dental Association, Jonathan Evans, the Royal London Hospital Archives & Museum, National Archives, College of Occupational Therapists, Professor Killingray, Trafford Healthcare NHS Trust, Paul Ross, Simon Adams and finally Senior Project Manager Raymond Warburton of the Equality & Human Rights Group, Department of Health.

We would also like to thank Cecile Day MBE, who was the prime mover behind the project. Her passion, resilience and dedication made this book possible.